The Setting Sun

and the

Rolling World

'Shadows on the Wall', 'The Crow', 'The Mountain', 'The Hero', 'The Setting Sun and the Rolling World', 'The Lift', 'The Ten Shillings', 'Coming of the Dry Season', and 'The Accident' were first published in *Coming of the Dry Season*, Oxford University Press, 1972; 'Who Will Stop the Dark', 'White Stones and Red Earth', 'The Brother', 'The Mount of Moriah', 'Some Kinds of Wounds', 'The Victim', 'The Day the Bread Van Didn't Come', and 'The Flood' were first published in *Some Kinds of Wounds*, Mambo Press, 1980.

The Setting Sun

and the

Rolling World

Selected Stories by
Charles Mungoshi

HEINEMANN : LONDON

William Heinemann Ltd
10 Upper Grosvenor Street, London W1X 9PA
LONDON   MELBOURNE
JOHANNESBURG   AUCKLAND

First published in Great Britain 1987

ISBN 0 434 48166 1

02101033

Typeset by Inforum Ltd, Portsmouth
Printed and bound in Great Britain by
Billing and Sons, Worcester

Contents

1

Shadows on the Wall

Father is sitting just inside the hut near the door and I am sitting far across the hut near the opposite wall, playing with the shadows on the wall. Bright sunlight comes in through the doorway now and father, who blocks most of it, is reproduced in caricature on the floor and half-way up the wall. The wall and floor are bare, so he looks like a black scarecrow in a deserted field after the harvest.

Outside, the sun drops lower and other shadows start creeping into the hut. Father's shadow grows vaguer and climbs further up the wall like a ghost going up to heaven. His shadow moves behind sharper wriggling shadows like the presence of a tired old woman in a room full of young people, or like that creepy nameless feeling in a house of mourning.

He has tried five times to talk to me but I don't know what he wants. Now he talks about his other wife. He wants me to call her 'mother' but I can't because something in me cries each time I say it. She isn't my mother and my real mother is not dead. This other woman has run away. It is now the fourth time she has run away and tomorrow he is going to cycle fifty miles to her home to collect her. This will be the fourth time he has had to cycle after her. He is talking. I am not listening. He gives up.

Now the sun shines brilliantly before going down. The shadows of bushes and grass at the edge of the yard look as if they are on fire and father's features are cut more sharply and exaggerated. His nose becomes longer each time he nods because now he is sleeping while sitting, tired of the silence.

Father dozes, wakes up; dozes, wakes up and the sun goes down. His shadow expands and fades. Now it seems all over the wall, behind the other shadows, moving silently like a cold wind in a bare field. I look at him. There is still enough light for me to see the grey stubble sticking up untidily all over his face. His stubble, I know, is as stiff as a porcupine's, but as the light wanes now, it looks fleecy and soft like the down on a dove's nestling.

I was in the bush, long ago, and I came upon two dove nestlings. They were still clumsy and blind, with soft pink vulnerable flesh planted with short scattered grey feathers, their mouths open, waiting for their mother. I wished I had corn to give them. As it was, I consoled myself with the thought that their mother was somewhere nearby, coming home through the bush in the falling dark with food in her mouth for her children.

Next day I found the nestlings dead in their nest. Somewhere out in the bush or in the yellow ripe unharvested fields, someone had shot their mother in mid-flight home.

Not long after that, I was on my father's shoulders coming home from the fields at dusk. Mother was still with us then, and father carried me because she had asked him to. I had a sore foot and couldn't walk and mother couldn't carry me because she was carrying a basket of mealies for our supper on her head and pieces of firewood in her arms. At first father grumbled. He didn't like to carry me and he didn't like receiving orders from mother: she was there to listen to him always, he said. He carried me all the same although he didn't like to, and worse, I didn't like him to carry me. His hands were hard and pinchy and his arms felt as rough and barky as logs. I preferred mother's soft warm back. He knew, too, that I didn't want him to carry me because I made my body stiff and didn't relax when he rubbed his hard chin against my cheek. His breath was harsh and foul. He wore his battered hat and stank of dirt, sweat and soil. He was trying to talk to me but I was not listening to him. That was when I noticed that his stubble looked as vulnerable as the unprotected

2

feathers on a dove's nestling. Tears filled my eyes then and I tried to respond to his teasing, but I gave it up because he immediately began picking on mother and made her tense and tight and this tension I could feel in me also.

After this he always wanted me to be near him and he made me ignore mother. He taught me to avoid mother. It was hard for me but he had a terrible way of making mother look despicable and mean. She noticed this and fought hard to make me cheerful, but I always saw father's threatening shadow hunched hawkishly over me. Instead of talking to either of them I became silent. I was no longer happy in either's presence. And this was when I began to notice the shadows on the wall of our hut.

One day the eternal quarrel between mother and father flared up to an unbelievable blaze. Mother went away to her people. After an unsuccessful night full of nightmares with father in the hut, he had to follow her. There had been a hailstorm in the night and everything looked sad in the dripping chill of the next day. The small mealie plants in the yard had been destroyed by the storm; all the leaves torn off except the small hard piths which now stood about in the puddles like nails in a skull. Father went away without a word and I was alone.

I lay under the blankets for a long time with the door of the hut open. One by one, our chickens began to come in out of the cold.

There is something in a cold chicken's voice that asks for something you don't know how to give, something more than corn.

I watched them come into the hut and I felt sorry for them. Their feathers were still wet and they looked smaller and sicklier than normal. I couldn't shoo them out. They came and crowded by the fire, their little bird voices scarcely rising above the merest whisper. My eyes left them and wandered up and down the walls.

At first I couldn't see them but when one chicken made a slight move I noticed that there were shadows on the wall.

These shadows fascinated me. There were hundreds of them. I spent the whole day trying to separate them, to isolate them, but they were as elusive and liquid as water in a jar. After a long time looking at

3

them, I felt that they were talking to me. I held my breath and heard their words distinctly, a lullaby in harmony: sleep, sleep, you are all alone, sleep and don't wake up, ever again.

I must have fallen asleep because I remember seeing later on that the sky had turned all dark and a thin chilly drizzle was falling. The chickens, which must have gone out feeling hungry, were coming in again, wet, their forlorn voices hardly audible above the sound of the rain. I knew by the multitude of shadows on the wall that night was falling. I felt too weak to wake up and for a long time watched the shadows multiply and fade, multiply, mingle and fade, and listened to their talk. Again I must have fallen asleep because when I woke up I was well tucked in and warm. The shadows were now brilliant and clear on the wall because there was a fire on the hearth.

Mother and father had come in and they were silent. Seeing them, I felt as if I were coming from a long journey in a strange country. Mother noticed that I was awake and said,

'How do you feel?'

'He's just lazy,' father said.

'He is ill,' mother said. 'His body is all on fire.' She felt me.

'Lies. He is a man and you want to turn him into a woman.'

After this I realized how ill I was. I couldn't eat anything: there was no appetite and I wasn't hungry.

I don't know how many days I was in bed. There seemed to be nothing. No light, no sun, to show it was day or darkness to show it was night. Mother was constantly in but I couldn't recognize her as a person. There were only shadows, the voices of the shadows, the lonely cries of the dripping wet fowls shaking the cold out of their feathers by the hearth, and the vague warm shadow that must have been mother. She spoke to me often but I don't remember if I answered anything. I was afraid to answer because I was alone on a solitary plain with the dark crashing of thunder and lightning always in my ears, and there was a big frightening shadow hovering above me so that I couldn't answer her without its hearing me. That must have been father.

4

They might have had quarrels – I am sure they had lots of them – but I didn't hear them. Everything had been flattened to a dim depthless grey landscape and the only movement on it was of the singing shadows. I could see the shadows and hear them speak to me, so I wasn't dead. If mother talked to me at all, her voice got lost in the vast expanse of emptiness between me and the shadows. Later, when I was beginning to be aware of the change of night into day, her voice was the soft pink intrusion like cream on the hard darkness of the wall. This turned later into a clear urgent sound like the lapping of water against boulders in the morning before sunrise. I noticed too that she was often alone with me. Father was away and must have been coming in late after I had fallen asleep.

The day I saw father, a chill set in the hut.

There was another hailstorm and a big quarrel that night. It was the last quarrel.

When I could wake up again mother was gone and a strange woman had taken her place in the house.

This woman had a shrill strident voice like a cicada's that jarred my nerves. She did all the talking and father became silent and morose. Instead of the frightful silences and sudden bursts of anger I used to know, he now tried to talk softly to me. He preferred to talk to me rather than to his new wife.

But he was too late. He had taught me silence and in that long journey between mother's time and this other woman's, I had given myself to the shadows.

So today he sits just inside the hut with the sun playing with him: cartooning him on the bare cold floor and the bare dark walls of the hut, and me watching and listening to the images on the wall. He cannot talk to me because I don't know how to answer him, his language is too difficult for me. All I can think of, the nearest I can come to him, is when I see that his tough grey stubble looks like the soft unprotected feathers on a dove's nestling; and when I remember that the next morning the nestlings were dead in their nest because somebody had unknowingly killed their mother in the bush on her

5

way home, I feel the tears in my eyes.

It is all – all that I feel for my father; but I cannot talk to him. I don't know how I should talk to him. He has denied me the gift of language.

— 2 —

Who Will
Stop the Dark?

The boy began to believe what the other boys at school said about his mother. In secret he began to watch her – her face, words and actions. He would also watch his father's bare arched back as he toiled at his basket-weaving from day to day. His mother could go wherever she wanted to go. His father could not. Every morning he would drag his useless lower limbs out of the hut and sit under the *muonde* tree. He would not leave the tree till late in the evening when he would drag himself again back into the hut for his evening meal and bed. And always the boy felt a stab of pain when he looked at the front of his father's wet urine-stiffened trousers.

The boy knew that his mother had something to do with this condition of his father. The tight lines round her mouth and her long silences that would sometimes erupt into unexpected bursts of red violence said so. The story was that his father had fallen off the roof he had been thatching and broken his back. But the boy didn't believe it. It worried him. He couldn't imagine it. One day his father had just been like any other boy's father in their village, and the next day he wasn't. It made him wonder about his mother. He felt that it wasn't safe in their house. So he began to spend most of his time with the old man, his grandfather.

'I want you in the house,' his mother said, when she could afford words, but the boy knew she was saying it all the time by the way she tightened her mouth and lowered her looking-away-from-people eyes.

The boy remembered that his grandfather had lived under the same roof with them for a long time. He couldn't remember how he had then come to live alone in his own hut half-a-mile from their place.

'He is so childish,' he heard his mother say one day.

'He is old,' his father said, without raising his head from his work.

'And how old do you think my mother is?' The lines round his mother's mouth drew tighter and tauter.

'Women do not grow as weak as men in their old age,' his father persisted.

'Because it's the men who have to bear the children – so they grow weak from the strain!' His mother's eyes flashed once – so that the boy held his breath – and then she looked away, her mouth wrinkled tightly into an obscene little hole that reminded the boy of a cow's behind just after dropping its dung. He thought now his father would keep quiet. He was surprised to hear him say, 'A man's back is the man. Once his back is broken – ' another flash of his mother's eye silenced him and the boy couldn't stand it. He stood up to go out.

'And where are you going?' his mother shouted after him.

'To see grandfather.'

'What do you want there with him?'

The boy turned back and stayed round the yard until his mother disappeared into the house. Then he quietly slid off for his grand-father's place through the bush. His father pretended not to see him go.

The old man had a way of looking at the boy: like someone looking into a mirror to see how badly his face had been burned.

'A, Zakeo,' the old man said when the boy entered the yard. He was sitting against the wall of his hut, smoking his pipe quietly, looking into the distance. He hadn't even looked in Zakeo's direction.

'Did you see me this time?' Zakeo asked, laughing. He never stopped being surprised by the way his grandfather seemed to know everyone by their footfalls and would greet them by their names without even looking at them.

'I don't have to look to know it's you,' the old man said.

8

'But today I have changed my feet to those of a bird,' the boy teased him.

'No,' the old man shook his head. 'You are still the cat in my ears.'

The boy laughed over that and although the old man smoked on without changing his expression, the boy knew that he was laughing too.

'Father said to ask you how you have spent the day,' the boy said, knowing that the old man would know that it was a lie. The boy knew he would be forgiven this lie because the old man knew that the boy always wished his father would send him with such a message to his own father.

'You don't have to always protect him like that,' the old man growled, almost to himself.

'*Sekuru?*' the boy didn't always understand most of the grown-up things the old man said.

'I said get on with the work. Nothing ever came out of a muscular mouth and snail-slime hands.'

The boy disappeared into the hut while the old man sat on, smoking.

Zakeo loved doing the household chores for his grandfather: sweeping out the room and lighting the fire, collecting firewood from the bush and fetching water from the well and cooking. The old man would just look on, not saying anything much, just smoking his pipe. When he worked the boy didn't talk. Don't use your mouth and hands at the same time, the old man had told him once and whenever he forgot the old man reminded him by not answering his questions. It was a different silence they practised in the old man's house, the boy felt. Here, it was always as if his grandfather was about to tell him a secret. And when he left for his parent's place he felt he must get back to the old man at the earliest opportunity to hear the secret.

'Have you ever gone hunting for rabbits, boy?' his grandfather asked him one day.

'No, *Sekuru*. Have you?'

9

The old man didn't answer. He looked away at the darkening landscape, puffing at his pipe.

'Did you like it?' the boy asked.

'Like it? We lived for nothing else, boy. We were born hunters, stayed hunters all our life and most of us died hunters.'

'What happened to those who weren't hunters?'

'They became tillers of the land, and some, weavers of bamboo baskets.'

'You mean Father?'

'I am talking of friends I used to know.'

'But didn't you ever teach Father to hunt, *Sekuru?*' the boy's voice was strained, anxious, pained. The old man looked at him briefly and then quickly away.

'I taught him everything a man ought to know,' he said distantly.

'Basket-weaving too?'

'That was his mother,' the old man said and then silently went on, *his mother, your grandmother, my wife, taught your father basket-weaving. She also had been taught by a neighbour who later gave me the lumbago.*

'You like basket-weaving?' he asked the boy.

'I hate it!' The old man suddenly turned, surprised at the boy's vehemence. He took the pipe out of his mouth for a minute, looking intently at the boy, then he looked away, returning the pipe to his mouth.

'Do you think we could go hunting together, *Sekuru?*' the boy asked.

The old man laughed.

'*Sekuru?*' the boy was puzzled.

The old man looked at him.

'Please?'

The old man stroked the boy's head. 'Talk of fishing,' he said. 'Or mouse-trapping. Ever trapped for mice?'

'No.'

'Of course, you wouldn't have.' He looked away. 'You go to school

10

these days.'

'I don't like school!' Again, the old man was taken by surprise at the boy's violence. He looked at his grandson. The first son of his first son and only child. The boy's thirteen-year-old fists were clenched tightly and little tears danced in his eyes. *Could he believe in a little snotty-arse boy's voice? He looks earnest enough. But who doesn't, at the I-shall-never-die age of thirteen?* The old man looked away as if from the sight of the boy's death.

'I tell you I *hate* school!' the boy hissed.

'I hear you,' the old man said quietly but didn't look at him. He was aware of the boy looking at him, begging him to believe him, clenching tighter his puny fists, his big ignorant eyes daring him to try him out on whatever milk-scented dream of heroics the boy might be losing sleep over at this difficult time of his life. The old man felt desolate.

'You don't believe me, do you, *Sekuru?*'

'Of course. I do!'

The boy suddenly uncoiled, ashamed and began to wring his hands, looking down at the ground.

That was unnecessarily harsh, the old man felt. So he stroked the boy's head again. *Thank you, ancestors, for our physical language that will serve our sons and daughters till we are dust.* He wished he could say something in words, something that the boy would clearly remember without it creating echoes in his head. He didn't want to give the boy an echo which he would later on mistake for the genuine thing.

'Is mouse-trapping very hard, *Sekuru?*' the boy asked, after some time.

'Nothing is ever easy, boy. But then, nothing is ever really hard for one who wants to learn.'

'I would like to try it. Will you teach me?'

Physically, the old man didn't show anything, but he recoiled inwardly, the warmth in the centre of him turned cold. *Boys' pranks, like the honey-bird luring you to a snake's nest. If only it were not this world, if only it were some other place where what we did today weren't our*

11

future, to be always there, held against us, to always see ourselves in . . .

'And school?' he asked, as if he needed the boy to remind him again.

It was the boy's turn to look away, silent, unforgiving, betrayed.

As if stepping on newly-laid eggs, the old man learned a new language: not to touch the boy's head any more.

'There is your mother,' he said, looking away, the better to make his grandson realize the seriousness of what he was talking about. From the corner of his eye he watched his grandson struggling with it, and saw her dismissed – not quite in the old way – but in a way that filled him with regrets for opportunities lost and a hopeless future.

'And if she doesn't mind?' the boy asked mischievously.

'You mean you will run away from school?' the old man restrained from stroking the boy's head.

'Maneto ran away from school and home two weeks ago. They don't know where he is right now.'

Echoes, the old man repeated to himself. 'But your mother is your mother,' he said. *After all is said and done, basket-weaving never killed anyone. What kills is the rain and the hailstorms and the cold and the hunger when you are like this, when the echoes come.*

'I want to learn mouse-trapping, *Sekuru*,' the boy said. 'At school they don't teach us that. It's always figures and numbers and I don't know what they mean and they all laugh at me.'

The grandfather carefully pinched, with right forefinger and thumb, the ridge of flesh just above the bridge of his nose, closed his eyes and sighed. The boy looked at him eagerly, excited, and when he saw his grandfather settle back comfortably against the wall, he clapped his hands, rising up. The old man looked at him and was touched by the boy's excitement and not for the first time, he wondered at the mystery that is called life.

'Good night, *Sekuru*,' the boy said.

'Sleep well, Zakeo. Tell her that I delayed you if she asks where you have been.' But the boy had already gone. The old man shook his head and prepared himself for another night of battle with those things that his own parents never told him exist.

*　　*　　*

They left the old man's hut well before sunrise the following day.

The boy had just come in and dumped his books in a corner of the room and they had left without any questions from the old man.

The grandfather trailed slowly behind the boy who ran ahead of him, talking and gesticulating excitedly. The old man just listened to him and laughed with him.

It was already uncomfortably warm at this hour before sunrise. It was October. The white cowtracks spread out straight and flat before them, through and under the new thick flaming *musasa* leaves, so still in the morning air. Through patches in the dense foliage the sky was rusty-metal blue, October-opaque: the end of the long dry season, towards the *gukurahundi*, the very first heavy rains that would cleanse the air and clean the cowdung threshing floors of chaff, change and harden the crimson and bright-yellow leaves into hard green flat blades and bring back the stork, the millipede and the centipede, the fresh water crickets and the frogs, and the tiny yellow bird – *jesa* – that builds its nest on the river-reeds with the mouth of the nest facing down.

The air was harsh and still, and the old man thought, with renewed pleasure, of how he had almost forgotten the piercing whistle of that October-thirst bird, the *nonono*, and the shrill jarring ring of the *cicada*.

The cowtracks fell towards the river. They left the bush and came out into the open where the earth, bare and black from the *chirimo* fires, was crisscrossed with thousands of cattle-tracks which focused on the water-holes. The old man smelt wet river clay.

'It's hot,' the boy said.

'It's October, *Gumiguru*, the tenth and hottest month of the year,' the old man couldn't resist telling the boy a bit of what he must be going through.

13

The boy took off his school shirt and wound it round his waist.

'With a dog worth the name of dog – when dogs were still dogs – a rabbit goes nowhere in this kind of terrain,' the old man said, seeing how naturally the boy responded to – blended in with – the surroundings.

'Is that why people burn the grass?'

'Aa, so you know that, too?'

'Maneto told me.'

'Well, it's partly why we burn the grass but mainly we burn it so that new grass grows for our animals.'

Finally, the river, burnt down now by the long rainless months to a thin trickle of blood, running in the shallow, sandy bottom of a vlei. But there were still some fairly deep water-holes and ponds where fish could be found.

'These ponds are great for *muramba*,' the old man said. 'You need fairly clean flowing water for *magwaya* – the flat short-spear-blade fish.'

They dug for worms in the wet clay on the river banks. The old man taught the boy how to break the soft earth with a digging stick for the worms.

'Worms are much easier to find,' the old man said. 'They stay longer on the hook. But a maggot takes a fish faster.' Here the old man broke off, suddenly assailed with a very vivid smell of three-day-old cowdung, its soft cool feel and the entangled wriggling yellow mass of maggots packed in it.

'Locusts and hoppers are good too, but in bigger rivers, like Munyati where the fish are so big they would take another fish for a meal. Here the fish are smaller and cleverer. They don't like hoppers.'

The old man looked into the coffee tin into which they were putting the worms and said, 'Should be enough for me one day. There is always some other place we can get some more when these are finished. No need to use more than we should.'

'But if they should get finished, *Sekuru*? Look, the tin isn't full yet,' Zakeo looked intently at his grandfather. He wanted to fit in all the

14

fishing that he would ever do before his mother discovered that he was playing truant from school. The old man looked at him. He understood. But he knew the greed of thirteen-year-olds and the retribution of the land and the soil when well-known laws were not obeyed.

'There will always be something when we get where these worms run out.'

They walked downstream along the bank, their feet kicking up clouds of black and white ash.

The sun came up harsh and red-eyed upstream. They followed a tall straight shadow and a short stooped one along the stream until they came to a dark pool where the water, though opaque, wasn't really dirty.

'Here we are. I will get us some reeds for fishing rods while you prepare the lines. The hooks are already on the lines.'

The old man produced from a plastic bag a mess of tangled lines and metal blue-painted hooks.

'Here you are. Straighten these out.'

He then proceeded to cut some tall reeds on the river bank with a pocket knife the boy had seen him poking tobacco out of his pipe with.

'Excellent rods, look.' He bent one of the reeds till the boy thought it was going to break, and when he let go, the rod shot back like a whip!

'See?' the old man said.

The boy smiled and the old man couldn't resist slapping him on the back.

The boy then watched the old man fasten the lines to the rods.

'In my day,' the old man said, 'there were woman knots and men knots. A woman knot is the kind that comes apart when you tug the line. A knot worth the name of whoever makes it shouldn't fall apart. Let the rod break, the line snap, but a knot, a real man's knot, should stay there.'

They fished from a rock by a pool.

'Why do you spit on the bait before you throw the line into the pool, *Sekuru?*'

15

The old man grinned. 'For luck, boy, there is nothing you do that fate has no hand in. Having a good hook, a good line, a good rod, good bait or a good pool is no guarantee that you will have good fishing. So little is knowledge, boy. The rest is just mere luck.'

Zakeo caught a very small fish by the belly.

'What's this?' he asked.

'A very good example of what I call luck! They aren't usually caught by the belly. You need several all-way facing hooks in very clear water even without bait – for you to catch them like that!'

The boy laughed brightly and the old man suddenly heard the splash of a kingfisher as it flew away, fish in beak, and this mixed with the smell of damp-rotting leaves and moisty river clay, made the old man think: nothing is changed since our time. Then, a little later: except me. Self-consciously, with a sly look at the boy to make sure he wasn't seeing him, the old man straightened his shoulders.

The boy's grandfather hooked a frog and dashed it against a rock.

'What's that?' the boy asked.

'Know why I killed that – that – criminal?' he asked the boy.

'No, *Sekuru*.'

'Bad luck. Throw it back into the pool and it's going to report to the fish.'

'But what is it?'

'Uncle Frog.'

'A frog!' The boy was surprised.

'Shhh,' the old man said. 'Not a frog. Uncle Frog. You hear?'

'But why Uncle Frog, *Sekuru*?'

'Just the way it is, boy. Like the rain. It comes on its own.'

Once again, the boy didn't understand the old man's grown-up talk. The old man saw it and said, 'That kind of criminal is only good for dashing against the rock. You don't eat frogs, do you?'

The boy saw that the old man was joking with him. 'No,' he said.

'So why should we catch him on our hook when we don't eat him or need him?'

'I don't know, *Sekuru*.' The boy was clearly puzzled.

16

'He is the spy of the fish,' the old man said in such a way that the boy sincerely believed him.

'But won't the fish notice his absence and wonder where he has gone to?'

'They won't miss him much. When they begin to do we will be gone. And when we come back here, they will have forgotten. Fish are just like people. They forget too easily.'

It was grown-up talk again but the boy thought he would better not ask the man what he meant because he knew he wouldn't be answered.

They fished downriver till they came to where the Chambara met the Suka River.

'From here they go into Munyati,' the old man said to himself, talking about his old hunting grounds; and to the boy, talking about the rivers.

'Where the big fish are,' the boy said.

'You know that too?' the old man said, surprised.

'Maneto and his father spent days and days fishing the Munyati and they caught fish as big as men,' the boy said seriously.

'Did Maneto tell you that?'

'Yes. And he said his father told him that *you, Sekuru*, were the only hunter who ever got to where the Munyati gets into the big water, the sea. Is that true?'

The old man pulled out his pipe and packed it. They were sitting on a rock. He took a long time packing and lighting the pipe.

'Is it true?' the boy asked.

'I was lost once,' the old man said. 'The Munyati goes into just another small water – but bigger than itself – and more powerful.'

The boy would have liked to ask the man some more questions on this one but he felt that the old man wouldn't talk about it.

'You aren't angry, *Sekuru*?' the boy asked, looking up earnestly at his grandfather.

The old man looked at him, surprised again. *How do these milk-nosed ones know what we feel about all this?*

17

'Let's get back home,' he said.

Something was bothering the old man, the boy realized, but what it was he couldn't say. All he wanted him to tell him was the stories he had heard from Maneto – whether they were true or not.

They had caught a few fish, enough for their supper, the boy knew, but the old man seemed angry. And that, the boy couldn't understand.

When they got back home the boy lit the fire, and with directions from the old man helped him to gut and salt the fish. After a very silent supper of sadza and salted fish the boy said he was going.

'Be sure to come back tomorrow,' the old man said.

And the boy knew that whatever wrong he had done the old man, he would be told the following day.

Very early the following morning the boy's mother paid her father-in-law a visit. She stood in front of the closed door for a long time before she knocked. She had to collect herself.

'Who is there?' the old man answered from within the hut. He had heard her footsteps approaching but he did not leave his blankets to open up for her.

'I would like to talk to you,' she said, swallowing hard to contain her anger.

'Ah, it's Zakeo's mother?'

'Yes.'

'And what bad winds blow you this way this early, *muroora*?'

'I want to talk to you about my son.'

'*Your son*?'

She caught her breath quickly. There was a short silence. The old man wouldn't open the door.

'I want to talk about Zakeo,' she called.

'What about him?'

'Please leave him alone.'

'*You* are telling me that?'

'He must go to school.'

'And so?'

18

She was quiet for a minute, then she said, 'Please.'

'What have I done to him?'

'He won't eat, he won't listen to me, and he doesn't want to go to school.'

'And he won't listen to his father?' the old man asked.

'He listens to *you*.'

'And you have come here this early to beat me up?'

She swallowed hard. 'He is the only one I have. Don't let him destroy his future.'

'He does what he wants.'

'At his age? What does he know?'

'Quite a lot.'

She was very angry, he could feel it through the closed door.

She said, 'He will only listen to you. Please, help us.'

Through the door the old man could feel her tears coming. He said, 'He won't even listen to his father?'

'*His father?*' he heard her snort.

'Children belong to the man, *you* know that,' the old man warned her.

And he heard her angry feet as she went away.

Zakeo came an hour after his mother had left the old man's place. His grandfather didn't say anything to him. He watched the boy throw his school bag in the usual corner of the hut, then after the usual greetings, he went out to bring in the firewood.

'Leave the fire alone,' the old man said. 'I am not cold.'

'*Sekuru?*' The boy looked up, hurt.

'Today we go mouse-trapping in the fields.'

'Are we going right now?'

'Yes.'

'I'll make the fire if you like. We can go later.'

'No. Now.' The old man was quiet for some time, looking away from the boy.

'Are you all right, *Sekuru?*'

'Yes.'

19

'We will go later when it's warm if you like.'

The old man didn't answer him.

And as they came into the open fields with the last season's corn crop stubble, the boy felt that the old man wasn't quite well.

'We can do it some other day, *Sekuru*.'

His grandfather didn't answer.

They looked for the smooth mouse-tracks in the corn stubble and the dry grass. Zakeo carried the flat stones that the old man pointed out to him to the places where he wanted to set up the traps. He watched his grandfather setting the traps with the stone and two sticks. The sticks were about seven inches long each. One of them was the male and the other the female stick. The female was in the shape of a Y and the male straight.

The old man would place the female stick upright in the ground with the forked end facing up. The male would be placed in the fork parallel to the ground to hold up one end of the stone across the mousepath. The near end of the male would have a string attached to it and at the other end of the string would be the 'trigger' – a match-stick-sized bit of straw that would hold the bait-stick against the male stick. The stone would be kept one end up by the delicate tension in the string and if a mouse took the bait the trigger would fly and the whole thing fall across the path onto the unfortunate victim.

The boy learned all this without words from the old man, simply by carefully watching him set about ten traps all over the field that morning. Once he tried to ask a question and he was given a curt, 'Mouths are for women.' Then he too set up six traps and around noon the old man said, 'Now we will wait.'

They went to the edge of the field where they sat under the shade of a *mutsamwi* tree. The old man carefully, tiredly, rested his back against the trunk of the tree, stretched himself out, sighed, and closing his eyes, took out his pipe and tobacco pouch and began to load. The boy sat beside him, looking on. He sensed a tension he had never felt in his grandfather. Suddenly it wasn't fun any more. He looked away at the distant hills in the west. Somewhere behind those

20

hills the Munyati went on to the sea, or the other bigger river which the old man hadn't told him about.

'Tell me a story, *Sekuru*,' Zakeo said, unable to sit in his grandfather's silence.

'Stories are for the night,' the old man said without opening his mouth or taking out the pipe. 'The day is for watching and listening and learning.'

Zakeo stood up and went a little way into the bush at the edge of the field. Tears stung his eyes but he would not let himself cry. He came back a little later and lay down beside the old man. He had hardly closed his eyes in sleep, just at that moment when the voices of sleep were beginning to talk, when he felt the old man shaking him up.

'The day is not for sleeping,' the old man said quietly but firmly. He still wasn't looking at Zakeo. The boy rubbed the sleep out of his eyes and blinked.

'Is that what they teach you at school?'

'*Sekuru?*'

The old man groaned in a way that told Zakeo what he thought of school.

The boy felt ashamed that he had hurt his grandfather. 'I am sorry.'

The grandfather didn't answer or look at him. Some time later he said, 'Why don't you go and play with the other boys of your own age?'

'Where?'

'At school. Anywhere. Teach them what you have learned.'

The boy looked away for some time. He felt deserted, the old man didn't want him around any more. Things began to blur in his eyes. He bit his lip and kept his head stiffly turned away from his grandfather.

'You can teach them all I have taught you. Huh?'

'I don't think they would listen to me,' the boy answered, still looking away, trying to control his voice.

'Why?'

'They never listen to me.'

21

'Why?'

'They – they – just don't.' He bit his lower lip harder but a big tear plopped down on his hand. He quickly wiped away the tear and then for a terrible second they wouldn't stop coming. He was ashamed in front of his grandfather. The old man, who had never seen any harm in boys crying let him be.

When the boy had stopped crying he said, 'Forget them.'

'Who?'

'Your friends.'

'They are not my friends. They are always laughing at me.'

'What about?'

'O, all sorts of silly things.'

'That doesn't tell me what sort of things.'

'O, O, *lots of things!*' The boy's face was contorted in an effort to contain himself. Then he couldn't stop himself, 'They are always at me saying your father is your mother's horse. Your mother rides hyenas at night. Your mother is a witch. Your mother killed so-and-so's child. Your mother digs up graves at night and you all eat human flesh which she hunts for you.' He stopped. 'O, lots of things I don't know!' The boy's whole body was tensed with violent hatred. The old man looked at him, amused.

'Do they really say that, now?'

'Yes and I know I could beat them all in a fight but the headmaster said we shouldn't fight and father doesn't want me to fight either. But I know I can lick them all in a fight.'

The old man looked at the boy intensely for some time, his pipe in his hand, then he looked away to the side and spat out brown spittle. He returned the pipe to his mouth and said, 'Forget them. They don't know a thing.' He then sighed and closed his eyes once more and settled a little deeper against the tree.

The boy looked at him for a long time and said, 'I don't want to go to school, *Sekuru.*'

'Because of your friends?'

'They are not *my friends*!' He glared blackly at his grandfather, eyes

22

flashing brilliantly and then, ashamed, confused, rose and walked a short distance away.

The old man looked at him from the corner of his eyes and saw him standing, looking away, body tensed, stiff and stubborn. He called out to him quietly, with gentleness, 'Come back Zakeo. Come and sit here by me.'

Later on the boy woke up from a deep sleep and asked the old man whether it was time yet for the traps. He had come out of sleep with a sudden startled movement as if he were a little strange animal that had been scared by hunting dogs.

'That must have been a very bad dream,' the old man said.

Zakeo rubbed the sleep out of his eyes and blinked. He stared at the old man, then the sun which was very low in the west, painting everything with that ripe mango hue that always made him feel sad. Tall dark shadows were creeping eastward. He had that strange feeling that he had overslept into the next day. In his dream his mother had been shouting at him that he was late for school. A rather chilly wind was blowing across the desolate fields.

'Sit down here beside me and relax,' the old man said. 'We will give the mice one more hour to return home from visiting their friends. Or to fool themselves that it's already night and begin hunting.'

Zakeo sat beside his grandfather and then he felt very relaxed.

'You see?' the old man said. 'Sleep does you good when you are tired or worried. But otherwise don't trust sleeping during the day. When you get to my age you will learn to sleep without sleeping.'

'How is that?'

'Never mind. It just happens.'

Suddenly, sitting in silence with the old man didn't bother him any more.

'You can watch the shadows or the setting sun or the movement of the leaves in the wind – or the sudden agitation in the grass that tells you some little animal is moving in there. The day is for watching and listening and learning.'

He had got lost somewhere in his thoughts when the old man said, 'Time for the traps.'

That evening the old man taught him how to gut the mice, burn off the fur in a low-burning flame, boil them till they were cooked and then arrange them in a flat open pan close to the fire to dry them so that they retained as little moisture as possible which made them firm but solidly pleasant on eating.

After supper the old man told him a story in which the hero seemed to be always falling into one misfortune after another, but always getting out through his own resourcefulness only to fall into a much bigger misfortune – on and on without the possibility of a happily ever after. It seemed as if the old man could go on and on inventing more and more terrible situations for his hero and improvising solutions as he went on till the boy thought he would never hear the end of the story.

'The story had no ending,' the old man told him when he asked. He was feeling sleepy and he was afraid his mother would put a definite stop to his visits to the old man's place, even if it meant sending him out to some distant relative.

'Carry her these mice,' the old man said when Zakeo said good night and stood up to go. 'I don't think she will beat you tonight. She loves mice,' he said with a little laugh.

But when he got home his mother threw the mice to the dog.

'What did I tell you?' she demanded of him, holding the oxhide strop.

Zakeo didn't answer. He was looking at his mother without blinking, ready to take the strop like Ndatofa, the hero in the old man's story. In the corner of his eye he saw his father working at his baskets, his eyes watering from the guttering smoking lamp he used to give him light. The crow's feet round his eyes made him appear as if he were wincing from some invisible pain.

'Don't you answer when I am talking to you?' his mother said.

The boy kept quiet, sitting erect, looking at his mother. Then she made a sound which he couldn't understand, a sound which she

24

always uttered from some unliving part of her when she was mad. She was blind with rage but the boy held in his screams right down there where he knew screams and sobs came from. He gritted his teeth and felt the scalding lashes cutting deep into his back, right down to where they met the screams, where they couldn't go any farther. And each time the strop cut into him and he didn't scream his mother seemed to get madder and madder. His father tried to intervene but he quickly returned to his basket-weaving when the strop cracked into *his* back twice in quick merciless succession. It was then that Zakeo almost let out a deafening howl. He closed his eyes so tightly that veins stood out in his face. He felt on fire.

'I could kill you – you – you!' He heard his mother scream and he waited, tensed, for the strop and then suddenly as if someone had told him, he knew it wasn't coming. He opened his eyes and saw that his mother had dropped the strop and was crying herself She rushed at him and began to hug him.

'My Zakeo! My own son. What are you doing this to me for? Tell me. What wrong have I done to you, ha? O, I know! I know very well who is doing this to you. He never wanted your father to marry me!'

He let her hug him without moving but he didn't let her hugging and crying get as far as the strop lashes. *That* was his own place. He just stopped her hugs and tears before they got *there*. And when he had had enough, he removed her arms from round him and stood up. His mother looked at him, surprised, empty hands that should have contained his body becoming emptier with the expression on her face.

'Where are you going, Zakeo?' It was as if *he* had slapped her.

'Do you care?'

'Zakeo! I am *your* mother! Do you know that? No one here cares for you more than I do! Not *him*!' pointing at his father. 'And *not* even him!' – indicating in the direction of his grandfather's hut.

'You don't know anything,' Zakeo said, without understanding what he meant by that but using it because he had heard it used of his classmates by the old man.

'You don't know anything,' he repeated it, becoming more and

25

more convinced of its magical effect on his mother who gaped at him as if she was about to sneeze.

As he walked out he caught sight of his father who was working furiously at his baskets, his head almost touching his knees and his back bent double.

The old man was awake when Zakeo walked in.

'Put another log on the fire,' the old man said.

Zakeo quietly did so. His back ached but the heat had gone. He felt a little relaxedly cool.

'You didn't cry today.'

The boy didn't answer.

'But you will cry one day.'

The boy stopped raking the coals and looked at the old man, confused.

'You will cry one day and you will think your mother was right.'

'But – ' the boy stopped, lost. The night had turned suddenly chilly, freaky weather for October. He had been too involved with something else to notice it when he walked the half-mile between their place and the old man's. Now he felt it at his back and he shivered.

'Get into the blankets, you will catch a cold,' the old man said.

Zakeo took off his shirt and left the shorts on. He got into the blankets beside the old man, on the side away from the fire.

'One day you will want to cry but you won't be able to,' the old man said.

'*Sekuru?*'

'I said get into the blankets.'

'The boy lay down on his left side, facing the wall, away from the old man and drew up his knees with his hands between them. He knew he wouldn't be able to sleep on his back that night.

'Thirteen,' the old man said, shaking his head.

'*Sekuru?*'

'Sleep now. I must have been dreaming.'

Zakeo pulled the smoke-and-tobacco-smelling ancient blankets over his head.

26

'Who doesn't want to cry a good cry once in a while but there are just not enough tears to go round all of us?'

'*Sekuru?*'

'You still awake?'

'Yes.'

'You want to go school?'

'No.'

'Go to sleep then.'

'I can't.'

'Why?'

'I just can't.'

'Try. It's good for you. Think of fishing.'

'Yes, *Sekuru*.'

'Or mouse-trapping.'

'And hunting?'

'Yes. Think all you like of hunting.'

'You will take me hunting some day, won't you *Sekuru?*'

'Yes,' the old man said and then after some time, 'When the moon becomes your mother's necklace.'

'You spoke, *Sekuru?*'

'I said yes.'

'Thank you, *Sekuru*. Thank you very much.'

'Thank you, *Sekuru*, thank you very much,' the old man mimicked the boy, shook his head sadly – knowing that the following day the boy would be going to school. Soon, he too was fast asleep, dreaming of that mountain which he had never been able to climb since he was a boy.

— 3 —

The Crow

Up the river was a crow in a nest. For days we had watched the mates building this nest with little twigs and bits of old rags. We did a lot of shooting then, and I don't know why we did not think of shooting the birds while they were still building the nest.

We do not eat crows, and birds or animals that people do not eat are associated with the night and witchcraft in our country. The crow is very greedy. In the bush we often used to come upon some nuts it had stolen out of the fields and hidden. We could have killed it because it is a thief. But its colour – black – is always frightening and it was safer to leave it alone.

But what made us want to kill that crow in its nest by the river I still don't know.

We went into the bush before sunrise that Sunday morning. The grass drooped with the weight of the heavy dew that had fallen in the night and the trees in the west showed the ripe tint of coming day. Under the trees it was still dark and a little chilly. It was very quiet and this made us quieter too. Quieter and a little afraid of things of the night and premonitions of bad things to come. One thing we were afraid of: father and mother had gone to church and left orders that we should follow. But we had planned to go hunting instead.

As I said, we were very quiet. Then suddenly out of the dark trees by the silver-hued pool the crow rose out of its nest and alighted in a tree up the river. The rushing sound of a big winged bird left our hearts palpitating for a while. Then Chiko smiled to show that it was just a crow and he was not as afraid as I was.

Quickly I said: 'The crow.'

'I know,' he said.

'Let's shoot it,' I said, and although I was afraid of my daring, I looked at him to see how he would take the challenge.

'Let's.'

We were both afraid but it was a code between us not to show each other that we were afraid.

Before we could get to the tree where it was, the crow rose again and was away to another tree further up the river. We ran after it, skirting with quick care the thorn bushes growing on the bank of the river. Now we were approaching the tree and the crow had not risen but we could not see it.

'Sh,' Chiko said.

'I'm not talking,' I answered back.

All of a sudden the branches of the tree stirred and the crow was flying back towards its nest.

'You talked . . . ' Chiko accused.

'I . . . ' But we were running back again. We could not see the crow but we knew it had settled in the trees where its nest was.

Under the trees we held our breath, stepped carefully so as not to snap any twigs and carefully looked into the nest.

The crow was not there.

We looked at each other. Silently we agreed that it was somewhere in these trees and silently we asked each other whether we should go on with this mad business; and again each of us was a little afraid of the other and we pretended that we were not afraid of a crow.

We went round under the trees. I saw Chiko aiming his catapult. I could not see the crow, so my heart stretched with Chiko's catapult, knowing, as I always know when shooting birds, that the crow would see him first and the pebble would hit an empty target. It was as I thought.

'I hit it!' Chiko exclaimed.

A lone feather floated down to us but the crow was gone. In its fear,

29

the crow might have had this one feather hooked and plucked off by a branch.

We came out into the open and saw it settling in a tree away from the river, towards the forest. This time it saw us coming, running in the open grass between the river and the forest. We would have been relieved to give it up had it flown further into the forest but it flew again towards the river and settled in another clump of trees.

'You go that way and I'll go this way,' Chiko said.

We had it between us.

I saw it first. Its mouth was open and its bird-throat moved. I could almost hear it breathing. I saw its black eye.

I tried to load my catapult and the pebble fell out of my fingers. I saw Chiko coming from the other side – only his head. He saw me loading. He must have seen it too because I heard the branches creak and the leaves rush.

'Have you hit it?' I asked.

'A branch got in my way.'

Now the crow flew a long way, still up the river, and we followed it, running.

It hid a long time in the trees and we were a long time looking for it, with it probably seeing us but not flying away, resting. And when it was rested it disturbed us again with its sudden rush.

We were getting tired but we were all of a sudden very serious about hitting it.

Again it went to the trees where its nest was but did not settle in the nest.

We saw where it went into the trees and we found it there. I aimed at its black eye. There was a soft plunk – the sure feeling of a dead hit. The bird, dislodged, made as if to fall through the network of branches but somewhere in the air between the lowest branches and the ground it stretched its wings and flew away. Several feathers floated to us.

'I hit it,' I said.

'It's got away again,' Chiko said.

30

'I'm sure I hit it in the leg or somewhere.'

Once again we were running. This time the crow did not fly very far and I knew I had hit it. But it always saw us first and was away before we could get to it. It flew very low: now here, now there, but we wouldn't give up. We were quite soaked with sweat and this running had ceased to be fun. It had become something that had to be done: the killing of the crow. We would have been glad if somebody had come along and told us to stop all this madness and go home. But there were only the two of us, our obsession, our fears and the crow. It had to die.

After I don't know how long, when we had almost given up hope of ever killing it, we finally hit it in the trees where it had made its nest. Both of us saw it at the same time and both of us missed it. It did not fly away. It just made a little uncomfortable movement and settled again, its mouth open and its throat moving.

Then Chiko hit it.

It fell and was caught by a branch and it settled again, one wing stretched as a chicken's is when you pluck off the big hard flight feathers.

Now it was so near that we couldn't miss it.

But we missed five times each, and felt silly when our ammunition ran out and we had to run and collect some more pebbles by the river.

Each time a pebble flew close to it, the bird just sort of hiccuped but did not move.

It was Chiko who finally dropped it.

But it was not dead.

Its wing was broken, its leg too, and the soft feathers on its chest were matted with blood.

Now we could hear the ghastly death-sound it made and its eyes were shiny black.

We hit it several times on the ground and each time we hit it it was in the body. It was a bloody mess. We aimed for the head but we always hit it in the body.

Now, all of a sudden, something got into us and we were fighting

31

the crow. It was no longer fun. In fact, I don't know whether there had been a single moment in the whole business when we had thought it was fun. We were grim and sweaty. We wanted it to shut off its death-voice. We were angry and a newer fear had just come into us. It seemed as if we had started something that was beyond us. In a frenzy we picked up the pebbles that we had used and hit it again and again.

But the crow would not die.

All of a sudden, its mate cawed above us. We almost ran away. But instead the bird must have heard us because it immediately flew away into the forest.

Chiko took a stick and hit the bird's head till it was all bloody.

But the crow was still alive.

I picked up a forked stick and pinned the bird's neck to the ground. I pushed and twisted but I could feel that the neck was very strong and would not snap.

We did not know what to do. We couldn't leave it like that.

Then Chiko got mad.

When Chiko is angry with anything – say a slow ox – he hits it with everything he's got – hands, head, legs, sticks, stones – and all the time he makes a sound in his throat, and if the ox won't move he bursts into tears and you can hear him cursing through his tears and hitting the ox, getting madder and madder with each whack until he bursts out into real bawling as if *he* had been hit.

He was exactly like that with this crow that would not die.

Finally we had to throw it in the river without knowing whether it was still alive or dead.

We ran out into the open. It was already midday. Chiko was crying. He had thrown his catapult into the river together with the bird. I felt shame holding mine as if to reproach him. There was no more fun in proving myself tougher than he was, so to be equal I threw my catapult after Chiko's into the river. I suddenly smelled hot blood in my nose but I wasn't bleeding. It is the way I feel when everything goes wrong and I am afraid.

4

White Stones
and Red Earth

All the way, on the bus from Marondera, rushing through the flat yellow-brown grass country, so different from his own, with isolated clumps of trees in undulating plains as far as the eye could see, through patches of eucalyptus or pine trees by the roadside; past small white redroofed towns with a sad yellowish dry season sun shivering far to the north of them, seeing an occasional granite-rock hill rising out of the shimmering flatness – white and grey – and always following the grey miraged road which twisted gently or went straight for mile after mile, falling or climbing gently – so gently you sometimes missed the rise or fall – all this passing by through the window, he was able to forget momentarily, the purpose of this sudden forced journey home.

He listened to the unchanging mile-grinding roar of the bus which lulled and soothed him into a deep repose which had, however, a melancholy tinge to it.

Bishi looked round. Most of the passengers were dozing in their seats. But he couldn't sleep. Not to think about it seemed to him heartless. But to pretend a sorrow that wasn't naturally there seemed to him worse than a betrayal of his brother. Yet in the kind of situation that he was now in, he was supposed to show some signs of sorrow. Bishi didn't know what to do. So he vacillated between two emotions: the elation that speed evoked in him and the guilty feeling that he shouldn't be feeling this way with what lay ahead of him . . .

★　　★　　★

33

They had been out camping by the river for three days and now they were returning to the school, singing and shouting. They were quite happy. And as they entered the dormitory he felt that something was terribly wrong by the way the other boys who had remained behind stared at him. Unaccustomed to receiving such concerted attention to himself, Bishi was embarrassed and confused. He could feel the skin round his mouth tightening into a question which he couldn't utter. There was an air of conspiracy and mystery among his classmates and some of the older boys in the upper classes.

'What is it?' Bishi couldn't hold the strain any longer.

Somebody, unsmiling, said: 'He looks very cheerful. I don't think he has heard it.'

'He couldn't have heard anything in the bush.'

Bishi looked from one to the other of the faces that were fixed on him. Then an older boy asked: 'You haven't heard from home lately, have you, Bishi?'

'No. Why?'

There was an exchange of looks: questions and several answering questions as if all of them were up in the headmaster's office for some prank and they were afraid to say who had started it all. Then one of the older boys took the responsibility and told him: 'Your brother is dead.'

They were all looking at him. It didn't make any impression on him. Because of the way they looked at him – as if they were surprised that he didn't make some show of sorrow of some sort, he asked: 'Who?' Somehow it sounded the wrong thing for him to say. But he couldn't think of anything else. He looked at the ground, aware of them all round him, waiting for him to break into tears or something.

'Your brother,' one of the boys said as if accusing him of something shameful that he had done. The word *dead* didn't make any sense to him. There was nothing in him that responded to the word but he knew that people cried when there was a death of someone close to them. He didn't have any tears in him. For the benefit of those looking at him, he tried to think of an incident when he had cried.

None came to his mind.

They were still looking at him, in surprised wonder, as he helplessly asked: 'Who brought the news?' That too was the wrong question to ask and he realized it when one of the senior boys said: 'They said it's Michael who is dead. You have a brother called Michael, don't you?'

He nodded.

'That's the one that is dead.'

And they waited while he tried hard to bring tears to his eyes.

So, there arose, in the foggy dusk of his mind, a white redroofed building under black cypress trees; a tall black tower that sent black writhing spirals of thick smoke through the black branches of the trees into the murky sky. There was no sun, everything was dark and close. It was this scent, remembered from another time, that finally brought the tears to his eyes. Nowhere in the tears was any memory of Michael but no one present there knew anything about this. They patted him and all tried to say something nice to him because his brother was dead. And of course the attention that they gave him had helped him cry harder . . .

Now, as the high veld country of Marondera, Macheke and Rusape got strangled and disturbed into the hilly sombre-grey dry season landscape of Nyazure, Odzi and Mutare – with hazy blue mountains rising here and there, and beyond, still hazier, written out as if in pale blue smoke, the deep red earth bared of grass by wild fires, dotted with black skeletons – as all this came into being and he knew that he was nearing home, a very deep and slow melancholy came into him.

With a rising sense of something bad going to happen in him, he watched the narrow grey road as it wound on ahead of him, carrying him on and on, now getting lost behind sudden ambush bends that made him sit up heart in mouth, insides suspended, expecting a head-on collision with an opposite-coming 'something' – the image in his mind couldn't be defined – it was something big and dark and blurry and furious and he felt relieved each time the bus turned the bend to find that the road was as clear and safe as ever. But the image never let go his mind.

35

He didn't like this country of low-lying clouds that sometimes hid the mountain-tops and the heavy mists that lay in the mountain hollows. He always felt that one day something would come out of these hidden places, something big and dangerous. He had often seen this in his dreams. . .

Five miles out of Mutare, at Christmas Pass, he got off the bus. No one else got down here. He watched the bus as it groaned up the pass and disappeared on the other side. There was a deep stillness. The road was bare. The sun was very low in the western sky. A creepy and chilly wind fanned his face and limbs. There was something, a little tiny thing inside of the wind that he could hear far away like a song he had never heard before, yet he was sure he had heard it somewhere but the somewhere wasn't on any known map. Then he dozed and it wasn't a dream that he dreamt but exactly how that place had looked like when his mother took him there long ago when he had the stomach troubles . . . the hospital.

It was a large building that just loomed there and disappeared somewhere beyond into the darkness of the trees. Painfully white and redroofed, it was set among age-scarred gum trees and very lean, straight cypress trees – only later did he know the name of these tall lean trees that he couldn't see where they stopped in the sky because it was all so shadowy and dark under them. As they waited with a lot of other people, surrounded with a lot of cries from babies somewhere in the building beyond, he saw the tower belching smoke a long distance away among the trees yet something inside him told him that the tower was also a part of this huge building because once upon a time his uncle Doro who didn't have the left foot had told him that they had cut it off and burned it at the hospital. That was the first time he had heard the mysterious word . . . hospital, and now, without his mother telling him, he knew what the tower that belched smoke was for.

And now there was a bed being pushed on wheels from one part of the building to another. Something lay on the bed, covered in blankets.

'What's that?' he asked his mother.

36

'What?'

He pointed at the bed, meaning the thing lying on the bed.

'Someone dead, I suppose,' his mother said and as soon as she had said it there was a sudden hush among all the people around them. Some made little noises in their mouths.

'Is it people who die in hospital?' he asked but his mother pretended not to hear it and she turned to a woman next to them and began to talk in hushed tones as if they didn't want to be heard. He could tell by the way they talked that something was very bad but he knew his mother wouldn't tell him what and he knew that it was also something to do with that tower and now there was also a sound in the trees, a small little sound that he felt he had heard before but he wasn't sure where and he had cried then . . .

The bus from Mutare woke him up. He realized he had been crying in his sleep and he quickly wiped off his tears and hurriedly got onto the bus trying hard not to let his eyes meet anyone's.

There were few people on the bus. They must have been all strangers because they were all very quiet. They were all old people and Bishi felt very small and awkward and embarrassed. He hoped one of them would recognize him and begin: 'Aa, I didn't know Marume had such a big boy . . . ' He went in and sat in the back where all the seats were empty.

The sky seemed to lower with the setting of the sun. The mountains seemed to draw closer with their hidden tops and misty hollows. They drove past Hartzell Mission, white and ghostly under gloomy tall gum trees with the mountain behind it looming darkly into the sky. Somehow the sound of the bus seemed to turn into a cat's low-voiced purring as if it were afraid to be heard. They passed on, through dead country towards the grey and black hills to the north, the black hills of home. They silently drove past the farm that was haunted and untenanted. There were stories about it: many came to look at it, even stayed for a few days before they just disappeared.

Far ahead of them, in the little light that was still left, in a lighter space set off by two dark masses of hills on either side of it, he saw a black still blob. As the bus got nearer the blob became a cluster, then a slow-moving circle of birds.

'Vultures.'

The voice startled Bishi. And before he could determine who of the old people in front of him had uttered it another one said: 'Carrion.' And these two sounds seemed to bewitch the bus which became even quieter.

Carrion.

Of course he knew all about vultures . . .

Somewhere in the hills in the wintry dusk the bus stopped to drop a man carrying soap-box boards with a black band on his coat sleeve and a stocking pulled over his head and ears. The man started off on an invisible mountain path, the wind tugging at his coat, and was quickly lost in the dark flurry of winter leaves.

Now, off the bus, he started out towards his father's farm, half a mile down this road. All round him the hills crouched nearer. And nearer.

Then the wind began.

He began to sing a hymn.

They heard him singing and they came out to receive him. They were just people in the dark and his mind made a suffering lump of all of them as they mumbled brokenly and shook hands with him.

'He is gone, Bishi.'

'Your playmate and friend and brother . . . gone.'

'Why has God no mercy? Now who will you turn to in time of trouble?'

'Gone, Bishi . . .

'Such a healthy boy . . . leaving us who haven't got long to go.'

'His wish and His ways . . . '

'Who shall you send to fetch water for you? Who will you send to the pastures to bring the cattle home?'

They were all the time moving towards the kitchen and he could smell the warmth of the people.

They were passing through the orchard. Dusk lay deep here but he

38

could still make out the fresh mound of earth under the silently swinging branches of the peach trees. He stopped and looked at it but he couldn't see much of it.

He allowed them to pull him into the kitchen where there was a fire and his parents and sisters and little brothers. They all rushed to him when he came in.

Nothing was very clear to him and he didn't cry then. They said all they had to say and he ate when they had all become quiet and his parents told him how Michael hadn't been ill for long at all before he died. Somehow, all this didn't seem to make any sense to Bishi. Something was closed in him. He was trying to see but everything was flat and monotonous. There were too many people around and they all seemed to be in the way – as if he wanted to go somewhere. All of a sudden he was very tired and sleepy. His mother noticed it and said: 'You must be tired.'

It was his father who put him to bed. Not that he was that young but it seemed to be something that his father felt he had to do. Bishi felt that his father was very exhausted.

'Comfortable?' his father asked when Bishi was neatly tucked in.

'Yes. Father.'

'It's tomorrow then, my son.'

'It's tomorrow, Father.'

This door closed. The outer one too. And now he was alone. The voices in the kitchen came to him muted but with great concentration he could make out what they were saying.

He listened for a very long time till he didn't know whether he was still listening to them or not.

And then somewhere in there, a long way from nowhere, the little sound of the wind came – the one inside the wind that came together with distant mountains in blue mist with hidden tops and hollows.

Bishi suddenly rose, put on his clothes and went out. He smelled freshly dug earth and the sighing of the leaves in the orchard. There was no more light under the trees but he knew exactly where that mound of earth was. He walked out towards it.

39

Bishi knelt by his brother's grave in the dark. He took a handful of the soil and began to knead it slowly in his hands. He did this for a long time and each time he put the lump of earth to his nose he seemed to be getting in deeper into the smell and then it just happened.

The whole lump of earth seemed to break up into something else that was nothing but its smell. He was holding the whole smell of the lump of earth in his hands and right at the centre of it there was the tiny continuous squeak of a mouse and a low but intense humming all round it.

Something broke in Bishi. His eyes burst forth and he shook with heavy sobs for a very long time.

They found him sound asleep on top of the grave early next morning.

Awake, he knew he wouldn't be able to put into words what he had experienced, but, somehow, he wasn't afraid any more.

5

The Mountain*

We started for the bus station at first cockcrow that morning. It was the time of the death of the moon and very dark along the mountain path that would take us through the old village, across the mountain to the bus station beyond. A distance of five miles, uphill most of the way.

The mountain lay directly in our path and was shaped like a question mark. I liked to think of our path as a question, marked by the mountain. It was a dangerous way, Chemai had said, but I said that it was the shortest and quickest if we were to catch the 5 a.m. bus. I could see that he did not like it but he said nothing more, to avoid an early quarrel.

We were the same age although I bossed him because I was in Form Two while he had gone only as far as Standard Two. He had had to stop because his father, who didn't believe in school anyway, said he could not get the money to send Chemai to a boarding school. We had grown up together and had become great friends but now I tolerated him only for old time's sake and because there was no one within miles who could be friends with me. Someone who had gone to school, I mean. So I let Chemai think we were still great friends although I found him tedious and I preferred to be alone most of the time, reading or dreaming. It is sad when you have grown up together but I could not help it. He knew so little and was afraid of so many things

* 'The Mountain' was first published in *Zuka 5*, October 1970.

41

and talked and believed so much rot and superstition that I could not be his friend without catching his fever.

From home the path ran along the edge of a gully. It was a deep, steep gully but we knew our way. The gully was black now and in the darkness the path along its rim was whitish. You never know how much you notice things on a path: rocks, sticking-out roots of trees, holes, etc., until you walk that path at night. Then your feet grow eyes and you skirt and jump obstacles as easily as if it were broad daylight.

On our right, away into the distance, was bush and short grass and boulders and other smaller gullies and low hills that we could not see clearly. Ahead of us dawn was coming up beyond the mountain but it would be long, not till almost sunrise, before the people in the old village saw the light. The mountain cast a deep shadow over the village.

We walked along in silence but I knew Chemai was afraid all the time and very angry with me. He kept looking warily over his shoulder and stopping now and then to listen and say, 'What's that?' although there was nothing. The night was perfectly still except for the cocks crowing behind us or way ahead of us in the old village. We barely made any noise in our rubber-soled canvas shoes. It can be irritating when someone you are walking with goes on talking when you don't want to – especially at night. There was nothing to be afraid of but he behaved as if there was. And then he began to talk about the Spirit of the Mountain.

He was talking of the legendary gold mine (although I didn't believe in it, really) that the Europeans had failed to drill on top of the mountain. The mountain had been the home of the ruling ancestors of this land and the gold was supposed to be theirs. No stranger could touch it, the people said. We had heard these things when we were children but Chemai told them as if I were a stranger, as if I knew nothing at all. And to annoy him, because he was annoying me, I said,

'Oh, fibs. That's all lies.'

He started as if I had said something I would be sorry for. 'But there are the holes and shallow pits that they dug to prove it.'

'Who dug?'

'The Europeans. They wanted to have the gold but the Spirit would not let them have it.'

'They found no gold. That's why they left,' I said.

'If you climb the mountain you will see the holes, the iron ropes and iron girders that they abandoned when the Spirit of the Mountain broke them and filled the holes with rocks as soon as they were dug.'

'Who told you all this?' I asked. I knew no one ever went on top of that mountain – especially on that part of it where these things were supposed to be.

'All the people say so.'

'They lie.'

'Oh, what's wrong with you? You know it's true but just because you have been to school you think you know better.'

I knew he was angry now. I said, 'And don't I, though? All these things are just in your head. You like being afraid and you create all sorts of horrors to make your life exciting.'

'Nobody has to listen to you. These things happen whether you say so or not.'

'Nothing happens but fear in your head.'

'Do you argue with me?' His voice had gathered fury.

'Remember I grew up here too,' I said.

'But you haven't seen the things I have seen on that mountain.'

'What have you seen?'

'Don't talk so loud.' He lowered his voice and went on, 'Sometimes you hear drums beating up there and cows lowing and the cattle-driving whistles of the herd-boys. Sometimes early in the hot morning sun you see rice spread out to dry on the rocks. And you hear women laughing at a washing place on a river but you cannot see them.'

'I don't believe it,' I said. The darkness seemed to thicken and I could not see the path clearly. 'I don't believe it,' I said again and then I thought how funny it would be if the mountain suddenly broke into wild drumbeats now. It was crazy, of course, but for no apparent

43

reason at all I remembered the childhood fear of pointing at a grave lest your hand got cut off.

It was silly, but walking at night is unnerving. I didn't mind it when I was a kid because I always had father with me then. But when you are alone a bush may appear to move and you must stop to make sure it is only a bush. You are not quite sure of where you are at night. You see too many things and all of them dark so you don't know what these things are, for they have no voice. They will neither move nor talk and so you are afraid. It is then you want someone older, like father, to take care of things for you. There are many things that must be left unsaid at night but Chemai kept on talking of them. Of course the teachers said this was all nonsense. I wished it were so easy to say so here as at school or in your heart as in your mouth. But it would not help us to show Chemai that I was frightened too. However, I had to shut him up.

'Can't you ever stop your yapping?'

We had crossed a sort of low hill and were dropping slightly but immediately we were climbing sharply towards the mountain. It loomed dark ahead of us like a sleeping animal. We could only see its jagged outline against the softening eastern sky. Chemai was walking so lightly that I constantly looked back to see if he was there. We walked in silence for some time but as I kept looking back to see whether he was there I asked him about the road that I had heard was going to be constructed across the mountain.

'They tried but they could not make it,' he said.

'Why couldn't they?'

'Their instruments wouldn't work on the mountain.'

'But I heard that the mountain was too steep and there were too many sharp, short turns.'

'No. Their instruments filled up with water.'

'But they are going to build it,' I said. 'They are going to make that road and then the drums are going to stop beating.' He kept quiet and I went on talking. It was maddening. Now that I wanted to talk he kept quiet. I said, 'As soon as they set straight what's bothering them

44

they are going to make that road.' I waited for him to answer but he didn't. I looked over my shoulder. Satisfied, I continued. 'And think how nice and simple it's going to be when the road is made. A bus will be able to get to us in the village. Nobody will have to carry things on their heads to the station any more. There will be a goods store and a butchery and everybody will get tea and sugar and your drums won't bother anyone. They shall be silenced for ever.'

Just as listening to someone talking can be trying, so talking to someone who, for all you know, may not be listening, can be tiring. I shut up angrily.

We left the bush and short grass and were now passing under some tall dark trees that touched above our heads. We were on a stretch of level ground. We couldn't see the path here because there were so many dead leaves all over the ground and no broken grass to mark the way.

I couldn't say why but my tongue grew heavy in my mouth and there was a lightness in my head and a tingling in my belly. I could hear Chemai breathing lightly, with that lightness that is a great effort to suppress a scream; almost a catching of the breath as when you have just entered a room and you don't want anyone in the room to know that you are about.

Suddenly through the dark trees a warm wind hit us in the face as if someone had breathed on us. My belly tightened but I did not stop. I heard Chemai hold his breath and gasp, 'We have just passed a witch.' I wanted to scream at him to stop it but I had not the voice. Then we came out of the trees and were in the bush and short grass, climbing again. I released breath slowly. It was much lighter here, and cooler.

Much later, I said, 'That was a bad place.'

Chemai said, 'That's where my father met witches eating human bones, riding on their husbands.'

'Oh, you and your . . . ' He had suddenly grabbed me by the arm. He said nothing. Instinctively I looked behind us.

There was a black goat following us.

I don't know why I laughed. Then after I had laughed I felt sick. I

45

expected the sky to come shattering itself round my ears but nothing happened, except Chemai's fear-agitated hand on my shoulder.

'Why shouldn't I laugh?' I asked. 'I'm not afraid of a goat.'

Chemai held me tighter. He was shaking me as if he had paralysis agitans. I grew sicker. But I did not fall down. We pushed on, climbing now, not steeply, but enough to make us sweat, towards the old village, into the shadow of the mountain whose outline had now become sharper. It was lighter than when we had started, probably third cockcrow, but it was still dark enough to make us sweat with fear.

'You have insulted her,' Chemai said accusingly.

I said nothing. It was no use pretending I didn't know what I was doing. I knew these goats. Lost spirits. Because I had laughed at it it would follow me wherever I went. It would eat with me, bathe with me, sleep with me. It would behave in every way as if I were its friend or, better still, its husband. It was a goat in body but a human being in spirit. We had seen these goats, as children, grazing peacefully on the hills and there was nothing in them to tell they were wandering spirits. It wasn't until someone laughed at them or said something nasty to them that they would file in a most ungoatlike manner after whoever had insulted them. And then when this happened it needed the elders and much medicine-brewing to appease them, to make them go away.

We walked on very quietly now. We came into the open near the old village school. The path would pass below the old church, and a mile or less on we would enter the village.

There would be no question of our proceeding beyond the village this morning, while it was still dark. I didn't care whether we caught the five o'clock bus or not. I just did not have the strength to cross the mountain before the sun came up.

Also I had to see my grandmother about our companion.

'Let's wait for daylight in the village,' I told Chemai. I saw his head bob vigorously in the dark.

My grandmother lived in the old village. She had refused to accompany us and many other people of the village when we moved

46

further west to be near water. She had said this was home – our home – and she would die here and be buried here and anyone who died in the family would be brought back to the old village to be buried. She had had a long argument with my father but she had been firm.

I did not like the old village nor grandmother Jape because both of them reminded me of my childhood and the many nightmares in which I dreamed of nothing but the mountain having moved and buried us under it. And then I would scream out and wake up and the first thing I would smell was grandmother Jape's smoke-dyed, lice-infested blankets that were coarse and warmly itchy and very uncomfortable to sleep in.

I rarely paid her any visits now, and I wouldn't have stopped to say hello were it not for the goat and my fear to cross the mountain in the dark. She would know what to do.

We were now below the church.

Suddenly the church gave me an idea. It had two doors each in opposite walls. We would try to leave the goat in the church. It was a further insult but I felt the risk was worth taking.

When I told Chemai he said he did not like it.

'I shall try it anyway,' I said.

'She will not stay. She will get out.'

We went up the path leading to the church door. We went in. The goat followed. I shouted, 'To the other door, quick!'

Chemai rushed for the opposite door. The goat followed him but stopped suddenly when the door banged to in its face. I slipped through this other door and shut that one behind me too.

Free. We ran for the village a mile up the hill.

Grandmother's hut was near the centre of the village. I knew my way about and in a short time we were knocking on her door, each time looking back over our shoulders to see whether the goat had escaped. I had to say, 'It's me, Nharo' before grandmother would open for us. 'Many things walk the night with evil in their hearts,' she had once told me.

'What brings you here in the middle of the night?'

47

'Nothing. We are going to the bus. We want to go to Umtali.'

'To the bus at this hour? Are you mad? You must be. . . ' She was looking behind us and I knew our friend had escaped. Quickly we slipped through the door, but the goat followed us into the hut.

Without saying anything grandmother was already busy with her medicine pots. And suddenly, safe and warm, I felt that the goat was harmless. It was just a wronged friend and would go away when paid. I looked at it. It was a small she-goat, spotless black. In the dim fireglow of grandmother's hut it looked almost sad.

Grandmother was eating medicines and Chemai was watching her intently. I felt safe. Somebody who knew was taking care of things at last. It is a comforting feeling to have someone who knows take care of those things you don't know.

—— 6 ——

The Brother

Tendai felt very excited as he knocked on the door. He was going to a secondary boarding school and he would be spending the last three days before schools opened with his eldest brother in the city. He knocked again. In his left hand he carried a paper bag full of food from the farm. There were two tins of peanut butter, one for him to take to school, and the other for his brother. There were cobs of green maize, some cucumbers and mangoes. In the inside pocket of his jacket were his identity card and travelling papers, a list of the things that his brother would buy him for school, and a letter to his brother from his wife. The brother had just married and the wife would be expecting soon. She was at home helping with the farm work. They had taken her too early from her husband and she was worried that her husband would not be there when she went into labour.

At the third knock, the door opened. Magufu, Tendai's brother, stood in the doorway.

'O, it's you,' he said. He didn't seem at all happy to see Tendai.

'Yes,' Tendai answered, slightly put off.

'Come in.'

They went into the house.

'I wasn't expecting you today. I thought you'd be coming tomorrow. Today isn't Sunday, is it?'

'No. Today is Saturday.'

They sat on the sofas in the living-room. There were some magazine pictures of naked women hung on the walls. For some reason, Tendai had expected to see some pictures of his brother's recent wedding. There were just those naked women pictures, a big portrait of his brother in dark glasses, like a black pop star, and some out-of-date calendars displaying more naked women.

It didn't feel like his brother's house at all. Not the brother who would drive the whole family to church every Sunday he was on leave.

Vaguely, Tendai expected some explanation.

'So?' Magufu was looking at him.

'So?' Tendai was startled. 'What?'

'I thought you said you'd be coming on Sunday – tomorrow.'

'Oh. Mother thought I should come today.'

'So it's mother, is it?'

Tendai didn't understand.

Magufu looked at his watch. 'Look. I am going out to meet some people right now. I was just about to leave when you came in.'

He pulled out a dollar. 'You know where the shops are, don't you? Right where you dropped off the bus here. Get yourself something to eat. Everything you need – pots, pans, salt – is right in the kitchen. I won't be long.' He was moving towards the door.

'I have brought some things – a letter from your wife – and . . . '

'I won't be long.'

Magufu went out and Tendai heard his car driving away. All of a sudden Tendai felt he missed home very much.

Magufu didn't come back until Tendai was fast asleep, after midnight: with a woman.

Tendai had to get off the bed and spread out on the floor. He had not quite heard his brother's coming in and shaking him and telling him to take some blankets off the bed and spread out on the floor because he had been confused by having to be awakened in the middle of a dream into the nightmare of a glaringly-lit room. Now, as he lay himself down and his head cleared, he realized that it was not his dream that had spilled into reality: the house *was* really full of people. There seemed to be a drinking party out there in the living-room.

Tendai turned thrice before finding a comfortable position. There

50

were voices of men and women in the living-room and they all seemed very happy because they were laughing and shouting and singing and now and then Tendai heard the noise of breaking glass.

His brother's voice seemed the loudest. Troubled by something he couldn't understand, Tendai drifted off into that uncharted world between sleep and wakefulness.

Later he woke up to the presence of someone in the room. He opened his eyes and saw his brother swaying in the doorway to the living-room. There were still some low voices all over the house, otherwise there was a kind of tired quietness.

Tendai smelt perfume.

He looked round.

She was sitting on the bed. Magufu was swaying in the doorway, half-turned, as if he was giving last orders to someone in the living-room. Then he turned, switched on the light.

'Please,' the woman pleaded, shielding her face with her hands. She was fully dressed, Tendai saw.

'Afraid of the light, huh?' Magufu laughed.

The woman didn't say anything. She kept her face in her hands. She wasn't a big woman. And she wasn't old either. From what he saw of her, sitting on the bed, her face covered and her head lowered, Tendai felt that she was younger than his brother's wife.

'A night mover, heh?' Magufu was laughing. He began to sing and shuffle on the floor, singing something about women of the night who shun the light, and shuffling in a drunkard's dance.

'Please. The light is killing my eyes,' the woman pleaded. She had a girl's voice, an abused girl's voice.

'The light kills their eyes,' Magufu danced towards the switch. The room flipped into darkness.

'Feel better? Feel safe?' Magufu asked, already half turning the words into song.

He shut the door and shuffled towards the bed.

There was the sound of the outside door opening and someone with good-humoured drunken violence came in shouting.

51

'Magufu! Hey, Magufu!'

The whole house woke up – laughing and shouting.

'Who's that?' Magufu shouted, swaying near the bed. He stroked the girl's head.

'It's Sam!' called a voice from the sitting-room.

'O Sammy-boy!'

'Wake up you louts! Wake up! Where's Magufu? I say – what's this? An hotel or brothel? My! My! My! Hey Magufu! Wake up and tell me what you think you have got here!'

'Get out, idiot!' Magufu shouted.

'Who is calling me idiot? Huh? Where is the unnameable obscenity that's calling me . . . '

'O Sam! Watch out. There's broken bottles on the floor.'

'Sam. O, Sam.'

'Where have you been Sam?'

'Good old Sam.'

'One of these days they are going to drag you out of Mukuvisi with a long knife in your back!'

'Hey Magufu!'

'Sam's here, Magufu.'

'Where's that black fart Magufu? Asleep is he? I'll teach him to . . . hey, Magufu!'

'Magufu your mother! Can't you fellows have respect for an honest, tired, hard-working man?' Magufu shouted.

'Won't you please tell them to keep quiet?' the girl said.

'Hey, Sam! Sam! The missus says you oafs shut up!' Magufu laughed.

'So you are there, are you? I'll teach you to leave a brother . . . ' Sam was banging on the door. 'Open up!'

'Please, Magufu . . . ' the girl pleaded.

'Sam's all right. Hey, Sam, you are all right, aren't you?'

'Open up in there or I'll . . . '

'Respect, Sam! Respect!' Magufu shouted, laughing.

The banging stopped. In a semi-sober voice Sam said, 'Respect, eh?

You said respect, did you, Mag?'

'You heard me, idiot!'

'But look,' Sam hissed, 'You can't do this to me, you know. It's not fair.'

'What's not fair?'

'Where the hell did you go? You nearly got me killed, you know.'

'Killed?'

'Dammit, Magufu. They are right out here in the van! And do they want to see you! O boy o boy o boy.'

'What are you talking about?'

'You know what I am talking about, you black this-and-that. And you know damn well that there isn't going to be any peace if you-know-who finds out that you have been knowing-what an unknown-who . . . '

Magufu sat up. 'You mean . . . ?'

'Yes. I mean she is here and you know what that means.'

Magufu whistled. 'Sam.'

'Yes ass?'

'Do our skin a favour?'

'And my reputation?'

'You know what your reputation is worth you this-and-that. Now, listen. Do us a real big favour.'

'You mean she is that you-know what?'

'I wouldn't be asking you if she weren't, would I?'

Sam whistled. 'You know, Mag.'

'Come on.'

'You'll get us all killed one of these days. You-know-who is really in one of her foul weather moods.'

'Sam?'

'Yes ass?'

'We are tired. We want to sleep.'

Sam whistled. 'Mag?'

'Uh – huh?'

'Is it worth breakfast with . . . '

There was a loud car horn blast outside.

'Get going Sam before . . . '

'I am on my way. See you at farting time!'

Sam went out shouting, 'So all you I-don't-know-what-to-call-you don't know where that idiot Magufu is, huh?'

'Go on Sam. We told you he isn't here, didn't we?' a voice in the sitting-room shouted after Sam.

A minute later they all heard the sound of a car angrily starting and driving off with three short blasts of the horn.

'Good old Sam,' Magufu said.

There was the sound of a bolt being shot home.

'You seem to have very good friends,' the girl said. She was still sitting on the bed.

'Come on. You aren't going to spend all night sitting there, are you?' Magufu was undressing in the dark.

Dimly, Tendai saw the girl standing up and beginning to take off her dress. Tendai looked away.

The bed creaked as Magufu got into the blankets.

'Come on. What are you standing there for?'

'Who is this on the floor?'

'He doesn't bite. Come into bed.'

'My things.'

'What about them?'

'Where shall I put them?'

'O dammit! Hang them on your nose and come right into bed.'

'I can't put them on the floor – it's the only pair I have.'

'You want me to take you right back where I took you from?'

'Please, I just. . . '

'You want me to take you back there?'

'Please Magufu,' she giggled and threw her things on top of Tendai.

Tendai heard her climbing into bed.

'I said take off *everything*!'

'Oh, please. I can't go to bed completely naked, you know.' She gave a short nervous laugh. 'It's only my pants.'

'Take the damn stink off!'

The girl gasped. She got out of bed.

'All right. If that's how you like it. All right. If – there!'

The thing landed in Tendai's face. A smell of sweat and very strong perfume. Tendai quickly removed it.

'Good. Now come into bed.'

She didn't move.

'Sheila! Sheila!'

The girl didn't answer.

'Do you hear me, Sheila?' Magufu's voice was thickening with anger.

Then slowly, terribly, Tendai realized that the girl was crying, trying hard to suppress violent sobs.

'Sheila? What's wrong?'

She didn't answer.

'Sheila! Sheila!'

'Yes?' Her voice was broken because of the crying.

'Don't you want?'

'I – I – don't . . . ' She sobbed.

'Come on, Sheila. Tell me, what's wrong?'

'Nothing.'

'Nothing?'

She didn't answer.

'I don't understand. I just don't understand.' Magufu half-rose in bed and leaned towards Sheila. He put his arm round her shoulders. She stiffened, caught her breath: 'Don't.'

'But why?' Magufu's voice was menacing.

'I didn't want to drink,' Sheila said.

'Are you ill or something?'

'No.'

'But . . . '

'Please Magufu. You won't beat me, will you?'

'Why would I want to do that?'

'If you find out that I am a big disappointment.'

'What do you mean?' Magufu's voice was very dark with suspicion.

Sheila didn't answer.

'Look, Sheila. I am not playing games any more. What's bothering you?'

The girl seemed to think for a long time, then said, 'All right then. I don't care. All right. O, it's all right.'

She crawled into bed beside Magufu.

'Hell, you're so small,' Magufu whispered.

The girl didn't answer. She seemed to be crying.

'What's wrong, Sheila? You ill or something?'

'I am all right.'

'No. You are not all right at all. You are shivering like a kitten out of water.'

Sheila didn't answer.

There was a long silence, then later on, as if she was being smothered, Sheila protested. 'Please Magufu. No. Please. No. No. No.'

'Why?'

'I – just – can't – '

'Why?'

She didn't answer.

'Why Sheila? I thought you loved me.'

'It's not that.'

'What is it then?'

She was quiet for some time then said, 'Promise me you won't be angry.'

'O come on Sheila.'

She thought for some time, then asked, 'You are married aren't you?'

'No.'

'True?'

'What the hell.'

'I have got to know, you know.'

'And if I am?'

56

'But *are* you?'

'Look. I don't see where this is getting us.'

'You are getting angry.'

'What's all this mystery talk about? I thought you understood when we left that place together.'

'Understood what?'

'That you were coming home with me.'

'I was drunk. You got me drunk.'

'So what?'

'I haven't been drunk before.'

'You would have had to start some day.'

'No. I don't think so. You tricked me.'

'O, come on Sheila.'

'You tricked me and now you say you love me but you won't tell me whether you have got a wife or not.'

'I don't see what my wife has got to do with this.'

'So you *are* married?'

'Oh, hell.'

'Where is your wife?'

'Come on, Sheila.'

'Does she know you trick people and when they don't know who they are and what they are doing any more you drag them home to bed and tell them to strip to the skin?'

'Look, Sheila . . . '

'And who is that Sam?'

'A friend.'

'What was he talking about?'

'Look, Sheila . . . '

'*What was he talking about?*'

'Look. If you're going to spend all night talking I am going to sleep, okay?'

'Why have you brought me here, Magufu?'

'You came on your own.'

'Did I?'

Magufu didn't answer.

'Where are my sisters, Magufu? You brought me here together with my sisters, didn't you? Where are they?'

Magufu didn't answer.

'Where are they, Magufu?'

'Look. Your sisters went out with some men and now shut up and let me go to sleep, will you?'

'They went with some men . . . did they say where they were going?'

'Sheila, you want me to take you back?'

'*Where did they go?*'

'I don't know.'

'How did I come to be here without my sisters? You have got a wife haven't you? And you let my sisters go away without me. Do you always do this?'

'Do what?'

'Drug people's drinks and when they . . . '

The slap was like the sharp crack of close thunder.

Sheila didn't scream. She held her breath as if someone had pushed her head under water, then she gasped.

'Take me home,' she said, gasping. 'I want to go back home. Please take me back home.' She was quickly getting out of bed and Magufu was holding her back and then she began to shout and scream and Magufu was telling her to shut up and there were two more short, slap slaps and Tendai realized they were fighting. They were now both on the floor and rolling towards him.

Tendai quickly got dressed and opened the door into the sitting-room. In the dim light from the street Tendai could make out shapes of people sleeping on the sofas. There was deep guttural snoring. The place reeked with the stench of beer. The whole room seemed full of sleeping people.

Tendai opened the door and went out into the street. He leaned his head against a lamp-post.

Then slowly, all the bile he had been resisting gathered into a tight

58

burning knot inside the chest.

He hit the pole again and again till his knuckles were sore. He hit the pole again and again till he was sweating.

Then he began to walk along the street.

There was the sharp smell of flowers from the trees lining the street. The leaves reflected the yellow light. The location was sunk in a drunken stupor, with the slightest hint of the stench of urine, stale vomit and human sweat. There was a low hum which told Tendai that even in sleep the township was very much alive, dangerously alive, but he didn't care.

There was a little hill at the end of the street. There was a church on the hill.

He found the heavy dark doors of the church closed. Through a window he saw that it was very dark inside the church.

He walked round the church into the trees at the back.

He lay down on a flat rock under the trees and looked at the lights of the town the other side of the hill. He found the garish brilliance of the city hurting his eyes and he looked into the deep moving darkness of the leaves of the trees above him. He closed his eyes and soon lost himself in the smell of the flowers and the darkness of the leaves. Something warm and comfortable moved into the centre of his belly and he felt very safe. He didn't care for the stories they told about township thugs and tsotsis.

He heard the sound of the leaves calmly soughing in the slight wind on the hill, and he slept, carrying with him the play of dull light and deep shadow in the leaves above him.

He woke up at the milkman's bell just a little before sunrise. His body was stiff and numb from sleeping on the hard rock. He stretched and yawned and felt his muscles and joints cracking. The city lights and street lights looked very weak in the eye of the coming sun.

His brother's house wasn't in his mind as he got down from the hill, so he walked round the location which at this early Sunday hour seemed to belong to children armed with loaves of bread wrapped in newspaper and the morning's paper.

59

When the streets began to fill up with older people looking sick and threatening from the heavy night, Tendai made his way to his brother's house.

There was a VW van parked in front of the house. Through the window Tendai saw a man lying between two women on a blanket on the floor of the van. They were fast asleep in their clothes. Tendai quickly looked away and passed on.

He tried the door and found it unlocked. He entered. There were two couples sleeping on the sofas in the sitting-room. Empty beer bottles were scattered all over the floor. There were broken bottles and cigarettes ends and ash swimming in dark splotches and puddles of beer. The air was heavy with the smell of beer, tobacco smoke, and something else that could have only come from the sleepers.

Tendai went into the kitchen where he found two women sleeping in each other's arms, their mouths wide open and saliva trickling from the corners. They lay on a dirty tarpaulin without blankets. A black pot lay on its side in a puddle of dirty water and there were lumps of sadza at their feet. Close to it was a plate with the remains of meal in it. On a little stand at the women's heads, right below the kitchen window, was a paraffin stove with a dirty pan on it. There were onion skins and pink stains in the pan. The lower end of the curtain had been burnt.

Tendai felt sick from the complex smell in the kitchen. He went out. He hadn't realized that women could out-snore men.

The door to his brother's bedroom was closed. Tendai didn't bother to find out whether it was locked or not. No one had stirred since he came in, and as he was about to go out one of the women stirred and sleepily said, 'Turn your lavatory mouth the other side.' The man didn't hear her and the woman turned away from the man and went back to sleep with slight sleepy moans and groans.

Tendai walked to the back of the house where he began to shoot imaginary villains and prodigal brothers with a shotgun as he had seen in Western films. The villains were too many for one man. They crawled out of holes and dropped down from trees and he was glad to

60

forget them as he watched the breathtaking thing that was the sun rising: so close, so big, weak and vulnerable and glowing without hurting his eyes. Tendai felt that the sun was very friendly and lovely as it rose, it only got angry as it grew older and climbed higher in the sky. He felt sorry for it. It couldn't help it.

He was so lost in himself, getting restless and angrier as the sun got higher and forbade him to look it in the face, that he didn't realize that they were all up in the house behind him.

A man came round the back and startled him with his 'Oh.' Tendai looked at him. The man's eyes were puffed up and bloodshot, his lips very thick with scales of skin and corn beer. He winked and grinned, shook his head and, as he passed water against the wall of the house, said, 'What a night' in a voice that sounded like gravel being unloaded.

There was a girl washing pots and plates at an outside sink at the next house. Tendai saw her giggling and pretending to be busy with the washing.

'Ohiyo – ouhgh! What a drunken terrible fanta – stic night,' the man said, stretching and rubbing his eyes and trying to stop the yawn.

'Your fly,' Tendai said, worried, looking quickly at the girl across at the other house.

'Oh, thanks,' the man said zipping it up, then: 'Hey!' The girl looked up at them. The man made come-here signs with his finger, making exaggerated motions of opening and closing his fly.

The girl stared.

'Want a sausage?' the man called in a loud whisper.

The girl giggled and went back to her pots.

'Good tail-end, eh?' the man said to Tendai, winking and nodding towards the girl.

Tendai left him and went round to the front of the house.

When he entered the sitting-room all eyes turned towards him, including his brother's. But no one said anything. They were playing cards at a long low coffee table in the centre of the room.

61

There were three men and two women playing and two more women who were sitting close together, sometimes watching the game, sometimes talking to themselves. They looked as if they didn't belong to the group, Tendai felt. They talked in very low voices, between themselves. Tendai recognized them as the women who had been sleeping in the kitchen.

There was an empty chair at the other end of the room. Tendai took it and went to sit by the window. He looked out.

They were playing seriously, tiredly but goodhumouredly, like people who have been together for such a long time that they need not discuss it. Except the two women who were not playing. One was tall and thin in a used sort of way and the other one was ugly, plump and pouting. They seemed to be disagreeing in a secret sort of way.

'Where have you been, Tendai?'

It was like a gun shot in quiet room. Tendai looked round from the window. His brother was not looking at him. He had the pack in his hands and was dealing the cards. All the others had their heads turned towards Tendai.

'Haven't you got a mouth?' Magufu said loudly.

'I have been out.'

'Where?'

'Just around.'

'Don't give me the lip.'

'O, leave him alone,' one of the playing women said. She was pretty and brightly brittle. She said, 'Is that your little brother?'

Tendai didn't like her voice. It was too high and brittle. Magufu didn't answer her.

'I said don't give me the lip, do you hear?'

'Yes.'

'You can do that sort of thing to mother and father but I am paying your fees and responsible for you from now on. Do you hear me?'

'Kick it under, Magufu,' one of the men said. He wore dark glasses and a thick beard. He didn't look as if he had been part of last night.

'I said do you hear me, Tendai?' Magufu wasn't looking at him.

'Yes,' Tendai said in a small voice.

'Come on, Magufu,' the bearded man said. 'Talk to him later.'

'I bloody well can talk to him anytime I damn well want and if it's now, it is now and who the hell is going to tell me not to?'

There was a terrible silence. Magufu had the cards in his hands. He slapped them hard on the table.

Everyone was looking down at the table.

'I said who the hell is going to tell me not to?'

No one answered.

'Magufu,' the bearded man touched Magugu's shoulder. Magufu violently shook the man's hand off. The man shrugged his shoulders. He looked round at the others. They lowered their eyes.

'Let's go, Dan,' one of the playing women said. She was small but hard and old. She had her hand on the knee of the third man, short, nervous-looking and frightened.

They stood up and left without saying goodbye.

The two women who were not playing looked at each other, said something to each other and stared at the men.

'Don't frighten the child,' the woman with the brittle voice said. She looked at Tendai, smiled, then looked round the room, and suddenly shouted: 'Where is Sam? Did any of you see where Sam's gone?' She stood up.

'Sit down Martha,' the bearded man said. The two women by themselves giggled to themselves.

'*Where is Sam?*'

Martha's voice was shrill. 'Did either of you see where Sam has gone?' She looked at the two women giggling between themselves. They didn't answer her.

'Am I talking to . . . '

'What's the trouble, Martha?' Sam entered. He came up to Martha and put his hands round her waist and pecked her on both cheeks. Martha closed her eyes and sighed, sinking back into her seat.

The two women laughed.

Martha looked at them hard and they shut up.

The bearded man smiled at Sam and Martha, absently taking the cards up. He began to shuffle them.

Magufu put his face in his hands and planted his elbows on the table.

'Where have you been, darling?' Martha asked Sam, picking at something invisible on his chin.

'Selling sausages, darling,' Sam kissed her but she quickly pulled away.

'Selling what?'

'Sausages,' Sam said lazily and tried to kiss her again. She slapped him hard on the cheek; 'I don't like that, ever! Do you hear me Sam? Don't ever bring the sausage joke with me!'

'O dear o dear,' Sam said. 'But they are in great demand.' He winked at the giggling women. They squealed brightly and clapped their right hands together in a popular greeting gesture.

'O Sam!' said the tall one.

'You kill me!' said the plump one.

Martha swivelled round and glared at them. 'Get out!' she hissed. 'Get out right now and don't ever let me see your dirty little tails again!'

Sam put his hand round her shoulders. She put her left hand round his neck. Sam winked at the two women. And they laughed into their hands, their heads down on their knees.

The bearded man smiled.

'Sam is my man and if either of you think you can repeat last night's scene with him you are getting out of town right now!'

'O, shut up, Martha!' Magufu roared, pulling his face out of his hands and glaring at her. Everyone looked at him, surprised, except the bearded man who was quietly shuffling the cards as if he wasn't there.

Sam looked at Magufu, suddenly very concerned and worried, then, just as suddenly, his face dissolved into its mischievous hangover.

Martha had stiffened, looking into Sam's face, hanging from his

64

neck as if he were going to drown. Now, Sam looked down into her eyes and kissed them shut. They began to play, whimpering like ecstatic puppies. The two women looked elsewhere, very serious.

Magufu returned his face into the cave of his hands.

The bearded man began to play a game they called solo.

'Tendai,' Magufu called, quietly, without taking his face out of his hands.

'Yes?'

'Did you see my letter?'

'Your letter?'

'I wrote a letter to father. Didn't he say anything to you about it?'

'No.'

'Are you sure?'

'Did it concern me?'

'Yes.'

'He might have decided to keep it to himself. Was it about anything you wanted me to do?'

'It was about money.'

'Money?'

'Your fees – damnit – haven't you got ears?'

Tendai said nothing. The others were careful not to look at Magufu.

'Didn't your father give you money for this term's fees?'

'No. He just gave me busfare to town, some pocket money and told me you'd fix the rest.'

'Including school uniform, toothpaste, soap, towels – and –?'

'Yes.'

There was a silence.

The bearded man was trying very very hard to concentrate on his cards.

The two women kept whispering into each other's ear now and again, looking away from each other, apparently disappointed, and constantly watching the closed door into Magufu's bedroom.

Sam had leaned back in his seat, his face turned up to the roof, his right hand absent-mindedly tap-tapping Martha's right shoulder as if he were trying to put her to sleep. Martha had gathered all her upper self on Sam's chest, eyes closed, left hand round Sam's neck and the right moving up and down, across and back his chest, inside his open shirt.

It was a tense moment.

The bearded man quietly reached inside his jacket and pulled out a bottle of brandy. He put it on the table and pushed it across to Magufu, and went to his cards without looking or talking to Magufu.

Suddenly Sam brightened and leaned across Martha: 'Aaah! The little blighter that's going to kill us all. And I thought we didn't have a single sip round the place. Good old Sando. How do you manage to pull out these wonders when everyone has begun to think the world is dead?'

Martha opened her eyes and said, 'What is it?' She followed Sam's eyes and saw the bottle. She sat up suddenly, 'Salvation at last!' She tried to reach for it but Sando held back her hand. She looked surprised, 'But why?'

'No,' Sando said quietly, firmly.

'Why not?' Martha shrilled.

'Because no,' Sando said.

'O, come on, Sando. Don't be hard on your poor old friends. We'll soon be dead anyway, why the Censorship Board?'

Magufu was looking at the bottle from above his fingers with only his eyes, the rest of the face still covered.

The two women nudged each other and looked at the bottle and then at the others. They looked as if they were watching the opening moves in a boxing match.

'Huh – Brother Sando?' Sam pleaded.

Sando was back at his cards. Whenever he turned round, the dark glasses were in Tendai's way. He would have liked to see the man's eyes. The man's firm calmness was beginning to frighten Tendai a little, in an exciting kind of way.

'Brother Sando? Do you hear me? It's your wee little brother Sam out here. There is dry dust in my throat and a chill in my belly, Brother Sando?'

Sando went on playing solo.

'Brother Sando, please!' Martha croaked. She was licking her lips and there was a big cord-like vein bulging out from below her ear down across her neck into the little cavity where the neck disappeared into the chest.

Magufu was still looking at the bottle.

The women were waiting, excitedly, a little afraid perhaps.

'Brother Sando!' Sam and Martha said together.

Sando quietly laid down a card on top of another and said, 'You vultures are a real hard boil in the innermost soft part of my arse's heart, you hear that?' He was very motionless, looking at the cards, but not playing. There was a slight tremor in the hands that held the cards.

Martha wriggled into some impossibly warmer and hidden place on Sam's chest, moaning to herself. Sam swallowed and said, 'No harm meant, Brother Sando,' and his eyes suddenly dropped out of his face into some cave inside his arid belly.

The women waited.

Slowly Sando turned towards Magufu.

He looked at him hard and long from behind his dark glasses.

'O damn you, Sando! To hell with you, Sando! Do you hear me, Sando? I said to hell with you and keep going don't you ever turn back because –' his hand trembling, reaching for the bottle. Suddenly Sando's hand flashed out and locked round Magufu's wrist in a grip that made both their arms shake.

Sweat broke over Magufu's face.

'All right Sando,' he whispered hoarsely. Sando let go Magufu's hand.

'Get us a jar of water Sonbiggy,' Sando called over his shoulder to Tendai.

Tendai went out to get the water,

'It's all your fault, Sando,' Magufu was saying, his face hidden in his hands again. 'I told you I don't want to touch the stuff any more. What are you doing to me Sando?'

'Nothing that you aren't doing to yourself.'

'O no!' Magufu was sobbing.

The plump woman whispered, 'Let's go, auntie.'

'And Sheila? We just can't leave her here alone with – with –'

Sando was looking at them. Their eyes clashed on the closed door to Magufu's bedroom.

Tendai brought in the jug of water.

'Get us some glasses, Sonnyboy.'

Tendai went into the kitchen to fetch the glasses.

'Your brother is very sick Sonnybig,' Sando told Tendai as he handed him the glasses. 'Every Sunday morning I have to come here very early to keep him company.' Sando was pouring little measures into four glasses. 'Tell you a secret Sonnyboy? Without me your brother would have killed himself. You saw me hold back his hand there? He would have taken that stuff straight and dry without a blink.'

Sando was adding water into the glasses. 'Don't you ever try it, Sonnyboy. This stuff is a killer. And don't ever try it alone. Share it with friends. Don't transfer your troubles to it thinking it will burn them. It will only create more trouble.'

Sando was handing the glasses round to the others. 'It's a real chariot of fire that takes you – in the opposite direction. Ever read the Bible, Sonnyboy?'

'Yes.'

'So you know about the Chariot of Fire?'

'Yes.'

'Here is one but harnessed to the devil's horses.'

Sando was screwing the lid back onto the bottle. He didn't give the two women any of the brandy.

'I am trying very hard to make your brother stop taking this stuff. It is bad for his health, and, lately it's been very very bad for his work.'

Sando sipped from his glass.

Sam and Martha did the same.

Magufu stared at his as if he didn't want to drink. His fingers were tightly curled in his face.

'You see, Sonnybig. This stuff is very bad for your brother. In the beginning it gave him a name and earned him admirers right and left in the drinking community. But now it's losing him friends fast, money faster and his health and sanity fastest. You understand all this, don't you?'

'Yes.'

'No, you don't. Not now, later maybe, but not today. This stuff, my friend, taken dry and straight at the rate you drink water in a day, completely wipes out any sense of self, shame, pride or dignity, wrong or right out of some people's minds. It also causes blackouts, the shaking of hands, sleepiness, loss of memory and a queer hating and avoiding of people, especially those dearest to one's heart. Conversely it breaks the loved ones' hearts into so many tiny pieces and throws them as far apart as heaven and hell.'

Magufu stealthily reached for his glass.

'Easy, Magufu, easy on it. Just a tiny wee sip to wet your tongue . . . that's right. Now, put it back . . . good.'

'It is very important that you understand what's happening to your brother right now. It's a secret between you and me. Don't tell your father or mother. You still have an expanding heart. You can accommodate almost anything if you try hard enough.

'Parents are a different thing altogether. They think they have seen the worst and now their hearts are built into little concrete squares that have no more room for expansion. If you tell them what I have told you about your brother you will only kill them. They haven't been taught to break the little concrete squares and make more room for emergencies like these.'

'Aren't we going to have something to eat here?' Martha asked. Her glass was empty.

'So, Sonnybig brother, don't let me ever hear that you have been playing over this song to Ma and Pa back home or I'll break your neck, right?'

'Yes.'

'It's not fair on your brother here and all of us his friends, right?'

'Yes.'

'One day, if you live long enough, you will learn that in this life you can only talk of certain things and leave out certain others about other people.'

Magufu put his glass down on the table. It was empty.

'Tendai,' he said. His fingers were now locked together between his knees with the elbows resting on the knees.

'Yes.'

'I am going to give you a letter to father.'

'Yes.'

'When are you wanted at school?'

'On Wednesday.'

'Today is Sunday morning. If you take the 3 p.m. bus you will be home before six. You will put up at home tonight and take the early morning bus back to town tomorrow – so around eleven you should be here. Tuesday I'll take a day off to do your shopping and you will take the Tuesday afternoon bus to school . . . '

'Aah, Sheila!'

'Sheila!'

The two women shouted together. Everyone looked up.

Sheila closed the door to Magufu's bedroom and came to sit between the two women.

'Hallo Sheila babe!' Sam shouted. His glass, too, was now empty. Only Sando seemed not to be drinking. He was concentrating on the game of solo.

Martha kept dangerously quiet but looking at Sheila with such a bright brittle look that one expected to hear the sharp breaking of glass any time.

'And how is our Sheila?' Sam said.

'Let's go Sam,' Martha stood up.

'Come on, Martha.'

'Come on yourself. What are we hanging round here for anyway? No food, no beer, no music. Come on, let's go.' She was tugging at Sam's shirt sleeve.

Sam looked up at her, narrowed his eyes and said, 'You know something Martha?'

'No? What? Come on, let's get out of here.'

'One of these very lovely days, Martha . . . '

'What is it?'

'Aren't you interested?'

'I am but hurry it up.'

'Sit down first,' Sam was smiling brightly at Martha.

Sando was looking at them.

Magufu was staring at his empty glass.

The two women were looking at Martha with open contempt. Sheila was looking for something in her handbag. She hadn't smiled or said anything since she came in.

'What is it Sam?' Martha said, putting her hand round Sam's neck and kissing him on the mouth with a bright brittle look at Sheila.

Sheila wasn't looking at them at all.

'O, I forgot to say hello Sheila,' Martha said. 'Hello Sheila!' she shrilled across the room and began to titter hysterically.

'Hello, Martha,' Sheila said, looking up and smiling sadly at Martha and going back to searching for what she could never seem to find in her handbag.

'Isn't Sheila beautiful, darling?' Martha told Sam, kissing him on the mouth again.

'Not as beautiful as you are my own dearest darling,' Sam said turning his mouth away from Martha's kisses, 'and listen darling. Remember what I said?'

'Yes. You said one of these lovely days . . . isn't that what you said?'

'Yes, exactly. You know you are very intelligent Martha.'

'Come on Sam,' Magufu said. He wasn't looking at them. 'Not

in front of the . . . '

' . . . and you are very very bright and I love you so much that . . . '

'Cut it, Sam!' Magufu shouted.

Sando was looking at them, not playing solo any more.

' . . . one of these fine lovely days I'll tan your hide so black and ram your teeth right back your mouth so they will be smiling north when you are going south!'

'Sam!'

Magufu's shout was too late. Martha was lying back on the sofa, her mouth looking as if she was eating raw liver. She looked too surprised to say anything.

Tendai saw Martha's lips swelling. He looked out through the window, his eyes filled with tears.

Martha didn't get up where she lay. She was very still. She turned over on her belly to hide her fast-swelling lips.

'Don't mess up that seat. Go and wash!' Sam told her roughly, yanking her up by the scruff of the neck.

'Leave her now Sam,' Sando said. 'She is all right now.'

Sam dropped her and she lay without a sound or making the slightest movement.

Sando poured brandy into three glasses. He added water and gave Sam and Magufu theirs. He emptied his in one gulp. Sheila and the two women were looking at them.

Sam downed his and winked at the women. 'Hi Sheila!' He smiled. Sheila looked away and the women giggled and then burst into loud laughter.

Magufu was studying his glass, not yet touched, in both his hands.

Suddenly, Sheila spoke.

Her voice was very different from last night, Tendai felt. It was soft, low and lost and it was worse than Martha's lips suddenly changing into overblown lungs.

'I had forgotten,' she said to her two friends, her sisters of last night – 'I had forgotten that it's my birthday today.'

They all stared at her.

'How old are you now, Sheila?' Sam asked.

'Fifteen.'

Suddenly the room was very quiet, everyone listening to but not looking at her.

'I had promised Connie and Rudo a party at our house. Now they will come and find I am not there.'

Silence.

'You drank too much last night,' the tall woman said unkindly.

'I was tricked. And you encouraged it.' She searched in her bag. 'I had never tasted a drop of beer or spirits all my life until last night. And you sat there while they poured that – what do you call it? – hot stuff into my Coke.' She pulled her woman's things out of the bag. 'Now, if only I can get those aspirins I hope by the time I get home nobody won't notice a thing.' She turned her bag upside down and shook it. Nothing dropped. 'Will just have to keep a mile's distance away from Father, though. No toothpaste will ever get this stink out of my mouth.' She stuffed her things back into the bag. She looked up straight at Magufu, 'No aspirins or anything for a headache in this house heh? Magufu?' She was smiling at him. Sam looked at her, at Magufu, then back at her and lowered his head, hiding something behind a forced cough.

'No. Nothing,' Magufu shook his head and quickly brought his hand to his mouth, tilted his head far back and knocked out the drink without making a single sound down his throat. The two women looked at each other in amazement. He banged the glass on the table and shivered throughout his whole body.

Sando was now very involved in his game.

'I am hungry. Is there anything to eat in here?' Sheila asked.

Magufu shook his head.

The women giggled.

'Or milk,' Sheila said. 'Haven't you got any milk – fresh milk?'

'Get her a bottle of milk Sonnybig,' Sando said tossing a coin towards Tendai.

'Thank you very much,' Sheila said. 'And – and Sonnybig – is that your real name? Anyway, no matter – Sonnybig – you are Magufu's brother aren't you? You are the one who was sleeping on the floor in there last night, aren't you? I remember that part – what I can't remember is the earlier part after everything was reeling and the lights were killing my eyes – anyway you, Sonnybig, please get me some aspirins if there is any change. Is that all right, Mister – if there is any change?'

'Get her some aspirins and a bottle of milk, Sonnyboy,' Sando said.

Sheila giggled, 'Sonnybig, Sonnyboy. Can't ever trust boys with too many names.' She put her head on her knees and was still.

Everyone looked at her.

'Let's have a game of Crazy Eight,' Sam suggested.

Sando dealt the cards and they began to play.

'Let's go auntie,' the plump woman said.

'Let's wait for Sheila's milk and pills.'

After drinking the milk Sheila rushed outside and was violently sick.

She came back and rinsed her mouth thoroughly with water, then she swallowed her aspirins.

'You promised to take us back to Chegutu, remember?' She was talking to Magufu.

'O, did I?'

'Yes. And you promised me four dollars last night after you hit me and I agreed to do what you wanted me to do.'

Sam looked up. His mouth dropped. Magufu looked at the cards that were becoming smudged in his sweaty hands.

'Your turn Magufu. Play,' Sando said. Magufu played.

'I think you have forgotten what I said,' he told Sheila.

'No. I haven't. Didn't he say that he would take us back when we refused to drive out here with him last evening, auntie?'

'You promised,' the tall woman said.

'You have to get us back,' the plump one said.

'Please, Magufu,' Sheila said. 'Forget the four dollars for last night

74

but please take us back to Chegutu.'

Magufu scratched his chin.

'Well – petrol. I haven't got any petrol. Have you got any petrol in the van, Sam?'

'Not enough to get us to Chegutu and back.'

'You can buy petrol, can't you?' Sheila asked.

'Yes – but –'

'Forget it girls,' Sando said, 'we are all broke.'

The women looked at each other.

Sheila put her head in her hands. When she looked up there were tears in her eyes.

'Look, Magufu. I said forget the four dollars you promised me when you thought I wouldn't give you what you wanted. Forget about driving us to Chegutu – just give me a dollar, I have got fifty cents here and I'll try and get a lift home.'

'Well – let me see. One dollar? Sorry. Can't help you.'

'But Magufu – just a dollar?'

'Honestly I don't –'

'Borrow from your friends then.'

'These are my friends and they too are broke.'

'Please.'

She was trying very hard not to spill any tears. 'One night is all right. I can always tell Father we stayed up late at Rudo's place and her parents asked me to spend the night – but two nights? Have heart, heh, Magufu?'

Then she did a terrible thing. She went down on her knees and, her hands on Magufu's knees, looked directly into his eyes.

'Have heart, huh? I did what you wanted. Came all the way from Chegutu with you, let you put brandy in my coke, danced with you, came here and spent the night with you – my first night ever – and you can't do a little thing like giving me a dollar to see me home to my folks, huh, Magufu?'

There was a silence. One of the calendars flapped against the wall.

'Sonnybig?' Sando said.

75

'Yes?'

'You said Father gave you some pocket money didn't he?'

'Yes.'

'You still have it?'

'Yes.'

'Could I borrow a dollar? You got more than a dollar haven't you?'

'Yes.'

'Can you get home and back on the remainder?'

'Not quite.'

'Well – you can use part of the fees father will give you –'

'The fees? But I am supposed to get fees from brother Magufu here.'

'Your brother hasn't got any money. That's why you are going back home today. You are going to collect school fees and money for your school clothing from Father. Now, lend us that dollar and I shall give it and any money you will have used on the way back to you tomorrow evening.'

Tendai handed Sheila the dollar.

'Thank you very much again,' Sheila said. 'Well, bye, Magufu.'

She didn't even say goodbye to her 'sisters' as she went out. The men went back to their game and later the two women also left without saying goodbye to anyone. Only a funeral party could break up this way.

Tendai went into his brother's bedroom to collect his jacket. The bed hadn't been made and there were some bloodstains on the crumpled sheets and right on the floor was a ball of crumpled newspaper with more blood on it. Tendai saw the letter from his brother's wife on the bedside stand where he had put it the day before, still unopened. He grabbed his jacket and went out.

'I am going now,' he told his brother without breaking his stride towards the door to the street.

'Hey, Tendai!' Magufu called.

Tendai turned his head. Magufu was smiling. 'If you have just a little surplus of the money you really need – you see we haven't got anything to eat here and –'

'I just have enough to get home on,' and he turned on his heel and fled from that house. He felt very desolate.

Later on he would forget some details of those people in his brother's house that day but he would always remember that something very violent had been done to him and that is when he had begun not to care very much for his brother Magufu . . . except that they had the same parents.

7

The Mount of Moriah

In bed, in his room, Hama couldn't see them but he could clearly hear them behind the closed door in the sitting room.

'Or you could start afresh. Get a job and work harder,' Matura, the medicine-man, was saying.

'I am not young anymore,' Hama's father said. 'These pains in my chest make it impossible for me to work or hope.'

'But you must have money to live on.'

'I know. That's why I am asking for your help. In the old days I wouldn't have bothered – I always had luck with the horses.'

'In the old days you had luck with everything. I never knew a man who had such luck as you had then.'

'But it's not there anymore now, is it? Lots of luck and no head with anything – money, women, jobs – everything – and today it's just as if I never had all that. One minute there – the next – gone.'

'You were a fool.' Pause. 'I have never met a bigger fool than you. You should have stayed married to one woman instead of taking them on and throwing them away the way you did – as if they were worn-out clothes you didn't need anymore.'

'I always felt that the women were finally more interested in my money than in me.'

'That was your trouble – and still is the trouble with you. Money. You didn't care for anything else. Not even those women. I could mention two or three who really loved you but you never saw it.'

'They never gave me any children. I wanted children and all of them didn't care for children. They were just after my money.'

'You never wanted any children. They saw that much through you. Even the body in there – you have called him the result of an accident. No, children isn't what you wanted and they gave you none. That's why none of them stayed for very long with you.'

There was a long pause, then Hama heard his father croak: 'You have got to help me. Something is happening to me, I can feel it. If I don't have money soon I'll be vultures' meat!'

Matura's voice was very soft – touched with a kind of sadness when he answered:

'Why don't you go back to the reserve? Don't you have any relatives?'

'None of them care for me. They would rather see me dead first.'

'You can't blame them. It's you who has thrown them away. In the same way that you have thrown away some of the best of those women. No, you certainly can't lay the blame on them.'

'Don't rub it in. I know that only too well.'

'No you don't.'

There was another pause, then quite simply, Hama's father said: 'I need help now. You have got to help me.'

'And how do you think I can do that? I am not God. Only your own people can help you now.'

'At least you can bring back my luck. Bring back my luck so I can play the horses again.'

Matura took some time to answer, then he said: 'That's going to be difficult. You have played with your chances in the past and it's going to be very difficult for you to have them back again. You aren't the only one in the world, you know. Your ancestors gave you your time and you lost it, now it's other people's turn.'

'Are you saying that it can't be done?' There was despair in Hama's father's voice.

'Yes and no.' Silence then: 'I am saying that this time you have got to pay for every little scrap of luck that comes your way – with your own life. This time you have to make sacrifices. And only few people are capable of making sacrifices – you know. You are not one of them.'

'I will try. I would do anything to have my old luck back again.'

'Forget it. You don't know what you're talking about.'

'I mean it.' It was almost a scream.

Matura laughed a nasty little laugh. He said: 'You don't have enough love to be able to make the sacrifice.'

'Love? What has love to do with it?'

'Everything. You see, you have got to sacrifice the thing you love beyond everything else to be able to bring back your luck. Now, what do you love beyond everything else? I bet you don't even love yourself!' Matura laughed again.

'My son . . . '

This time the medicine-man's laugh was really loud. He was enjoying himself. He said: 'Don't strain yourself. You don't love that boy. I have told you that already. You only feel that he is your responsibility. You crippled him, you can't get rid of the guilt so you think it's love. I think you even hate him!'

'How can you say that? He is the only one I have got!'

'We shall see about that.' Their voices were now very low.

In his room Hama turned over and looked at the yellow wall, then through the window at the peach tree whose bare boughs pointed as if in prayer to the sky. The room was turning into a dungeon. Hama hardly remembered a day he had been out of it for more than half a day since he came back from the hospital without his left leg. And now he couldn't even remember how long back that was. He couldn't remember how long he had been in this hateful room with its flecking yellow walls and damp, rotting corners curtained off with spider netting studded with dead flies and cockroaches. He couldn't remember how long he had been fighting the bedbugs and the fleas and the lice and the other tiny things that gave him sleepless nights, biting, bloodsucking and irritating him. The fleas and the bugs and the lice were all right. At least he could see them. There were those other tiny things that he couldn't see, that he couldn't tell whether they were inside or outside him. Once he had tried to complain about them to his father

80

and all he had got in answer was a very cold wordless look. Now he kept quiet. Even on the bad days when his father would come home complaining of how badly things were going with him, trying to trap Hama into talking, he would keep quiet. That had become a form of revenge on his father – and he could tell that his father hated him for it.

Hama was tired of his father. Most of the time he was only just indifferent to him. In the beginning he had cared: complaining that he wanted to go home to Aunt Rudo, that he couldn't sleep in this room or that the room needed cleaning – anything to attract his father's attention. But since his father never paid any attention to them, Hama had learned to forget that his father existed. Through all the time he had been living here with his father, Hama had been able to follow, at a long silent distance, his father's descent into the mud – from one woman to another, through God knew how many friends with whom he always parted violently and almost always at parties held in the house – quarrelling, fighting. And it was always over the same thing: these parasites were after his father's money, out to ruin him. Hama had slowly learned the cause of the friendships, the quarrels, the fights and the partings: money. 'My money' was a favourite phrase of his father's. He had heard it mentioned so much that even now, though he had never had any money himself, he violently hated what the word did to his ears: it was the sound of breaking crockery and furniture, of belching and vomiting, the stink of beer and stale vomit, the sound of a fist against a mouth so battered it sounded like a wet sponge – and blood all over the place. And the screams and the groans and the moans and the threats. He remembered too – from a very long hazy distance – and from constant reminders by his father – that it had been because of her incapability to use money properly that his mother had been sent away. Now he couldn't even remember how she had looked like. But he remembered her wet face. What he knew of her as a person he had got from his aunt, Rudo, where his father had sent him soon after the divorce. And any memories that Hama had of any time that he had ever been happy or talked at length to someone were of the time he had been staying with his aunt in the reserve. And he had cried and cried when his father came to take him away because it was time, his father had said, it was time that the boy went to school. It had just been a lie and Aunt Rudo had said it right there and then and he, Hama, had somehow known that it was just a plain old lie. Of course there hadn't been any school. Instead, there had been that terrible accident when his father drank while driving – drinking with that woman he had picked up in Chivhu, telling her he had lots of money and that he was going to marry her. There had been no school: only that accident where the woman had died in hospital and Hama had lost his left leg. And his father had escaped with just a cut on his chin where the beard wouldn't grow now so that his father – who had loved to grow his beard long – sometimes using black shoe polish to keep it really black – had to shave it clean off because the scar always showed itself at its worst when he didn't shave. There had been that accident and those long dreary months in hospital with his leg hung above him in plaster before he came to live in this room which had slowly become worse than the hospital. Aunt Rudo had once paid him a visit but she hadn't stayed long because his father had been nasty to her and she had gone back home the same day and she had never come back. And since that time, Hama had not seen anyone from home. Talk had filtered in through that door to him – talk of how his father had cast away his own people and the curse that his mother had put on him. Whether this was true or not, Hama couldn't say. All he knew was that there were nights when his father shouted in his sleep, ranting and raving as if he were talking to someone who was bothering him; and that there were times when his father called in strange people – mostly medicine-men and women – to advise him on some matters.

And this evening was one of those times. And this time it looked worse because this was the fifth medicine-man his father had consulted in a row. In his room, Hama had been able to gather that his father had long lost his job, owed a lot of money to people and that the doctors had told him to stop smoking and drinking because he had contracted some disease that would kill him if he didn't listen to them. All this Hama heard without his meaning to hear it – like so many things he had heard since he had come to live here. But like some of those things, this had stuck in his mind without his meaning to let it stick.

They were talking loudly again in the sitting room.

' . . . a very big sacrifice,' the medicine-man was saying.

'I will try. What else can I do?'

'Only his heart, a piece of his liver, his genitals. Mix them with this . . . ' And again the voices were too low for Hama to make out. But he knew what it was all about. He had heard lots like it. It was the good luck prescription. The medicine that his father wanted to be able to play the horses again. The medicine that his father needed to be rich once more. He had heard so many of these prescriptions in the past few weeks that he hardly paid any attention to what was being said right now. He was more interested in the scene that was taking shape of its own in his mind. He could see his father's yellow whiskers trembling and his tiny head bobbing up and down as if it were a gourd sitting on water, the yellow tobacco-stained talons digging into the wood of the table as visions of money, money and more money took possession of him till he just couldn't sit still, impatient to go out and try out this new medicine . . . Hama's heart tightened and he felt the little invisible insects inside him . . .

'Don't do it if you find you are afraid. You must be absolutely calm because one mistake might mean your death. I suggest that you see no woman, talk to no one, touch very little food before you perform the task. You must take care that no one sees you leave or come back. And you have to banish all worry from your mind. There is no turning back because once you do that – you are a dead donkey!' Then some inaudible words. Later, Hama heard them laughing. His father's laugh was very thin and nervous. Then the door to the street opened and shut. Hama's father stayed out very late that night and when he came back, Hama heard him talking to himself.

All that night, each time he woke up from his light sleep, Hama heard his father walking about in his bedroom, talking to himself.

★   ★   ★

Hama woke up when he heard his father's shuffling just outside his door. He mentally, without his being conscious of it, put on his armour. His father stopped and coughed, clearing his throat as if he had something very important to say. They were usually guilt-ridden requests to Hama to do something for him – little sedentary jobs like sewing some buttons on to his shirt or something of the sort. Hama never showed that he liked or disliked them.

His father coughed again and the door to Hama's room opened slightly. Hama looked away, pretending that he was asleep. His father came in and stood in his usual spot whenever he came into this room: close to the door as if ready to bolt out at the slightest hint of a threat on his life. He coughed again; that had become his way of saying good morning to his son.

'We are going home,' Hama's father said. For some time the statement hung embarrassingly naked in the air before Hama turned round to face his father. He fixed his eyes on his father.

'I have borrowed a car.' He took a step back from his son's staring eyes. His bloodshot eyes shifted off Hama's face and ricocheted off the boy's aluminium leg which Hama had thrust out of the blankets. His face twitched: 'This time there won't be any accident.' Hama looked away through the window at the peach tree. His father kept changing his weight from one leg to the other. Conversation with his son seemed to make him nervous. It was like climbing a very high mountain: he was a victim of vertigo. 'Don't you want to go home?'

Hama looked at his father silently and when he saw that he was about to repeat his question he said: 'Without your driver's licence?' His father's body jerked.

'Who told you?'

'I heard you talking to your friends in there.'

There was a painful silence, then Hama's father brought out a trembling hand and put it to his face. He turned away saying: 'Get yourself ready. I am going to bring the car round.' He almost slunk out of the room. Hama looked after him, wondering.

'Since that time he came out of the hospital they had never gone home. Had Aunt Rudo died? The thought frightened the boy and he lay very still and all of a sudden he heard distant voices calling to each other at play in the village dusk. Aunt Rudo?

The door opened again and Hama felt his father's presence in the room.

'Is Aunt Rudo dead?' he asked without looking at his father.

His father looked at him furtively, surprised, unsettled and hurriedly left the room saying that nobody was dead and he had to buck up because it was a long drive home and they had to get there before duskfall.

They drove out of Harare along Beatrice Road. It was a close day, very still and already uncomfortably warm in the early morning.

In dead silence they slid through early morning shadows of tall gum trees along the road. Hama's father looked solemnly ahead, driving carefully, and Hama studied his father's tensed-up face in the rear-view mirror. From his father's face, his eyes shifted to the grey road fanning out away from them, dappled with the shadows of departing night and the lights of coming day.

The sun climbed a little higher as they turned off the main road into a dusty easterly road. It was now hot and his father was sweating in his jacket. Hama resented him for not taking it off, because, by a weird association of thought he felt as if *he* was sweating and uncomfortable.

The lonely yellow road stretched before them in the scorching sun, so wide and so long that it gave Hama the illusion that they were not moving at all. Behind them the dust rose and hung in still clouds. The brittle grass and bushes beside the road were powdered yellow with dust and farther away from the road on both sides stretched plains of scattered trees and not much grass on the ground where the shadows of the trees were black blobs, cool and inviting. Looking at these dark patches of shadow, Hama felt comforted because he now felt as if he were sitting under one of those trees, in the shade out of the sun. He felt happy, and then, slowly, he began to feel sad because he smelled cattle and hay.

At Aunt Rudo's they were driving the cattle across the stream, bringing them home from the pastures in the dusty purple dusk singing 'The Mount of Moriah'. Aunt Rudo had taught him the song and had told him the story behind the song. Without actually singing it now, but with the tune going round and round inside him, he understood the song now better than that time long ago in the village. The length of the road – all that distance to be travelled – lent a kind of strange sadness – a sweet sadness – to the song. Moriah: a dark blue mountain in autumn haze across plains of dry tall grass where the earth meets the sky. Abraham: long-bearded, broad-shouldered, in tattered coloured robes – he had seen a picture once when Aunt Rudo had taken him to church – mansmelling of snuff, fire, sweat, wet soil and the open air with a kindly wrinkled face and the wisdom of distant horizons in his eyes. Isaac: small, eager, smelling of goatmilk cream, his supple boy's back arched under the heavy burden of faggots: asking: 'But where is the lamb for the sacrifice, Father?' And Abraham's booming voice: 'God shall provide, son.' And, thinking about this, Hama imagined himself as Isaac, but when he looked in the rearview mirror and saw his father's mean, worry-strained face he felt betrayed. His father was a far cry from the self-confident, big-boned Abraham. And if his father couldn't be Abraham, then *he* was not Isaac . . .

They were passing through a village, scattered here and there in the bush red-brick rondavels with thatched roof and an occasional glitter in the sun to show off somebody's big house with its corrugated iron roof, bare orange and white fields trembling with the heat of the sun, bordered with clumps of brown and yellow bush. And soon, this passed into dry grass plains, solitary, burdened with the heat, with an occasional acacia or *muhacha*, and always the illusion of water some-where – this from the dark ripe-rapoko colour of the grass – but no water at all, until, all unexpectedly, the car dropped and they were crossing the brown-pebbled, sun-burned red of a seasonal river, with, as the eye followed its course well-marked across the plain, a silver-fleck to show a stagnant pool of rust-coloured water, not any help for assuaging thirst. Further on, the plains had been burned. For many miles on either side nothing stood out in the thirstmaking shimmering blackness. 'The Mount of Moriah' died in the boy's mind and he grew silent and depressed. The road rose and fell, rose and fell again and again with the land as far as the eye could see and Hama smelled burning oil and felt the car rolling and shaking as if it would fall to pieces on the gravel of the road, ever so straight, so lonely, always and forever oppressed with the heat without any hope of any shade and he felt all the weight of the heat on him and it seemed to him as if they would never get anywhere and the sun would never stop burning and scorching everything black.

Then suddenly, the land broke up – gullies, a river: water!

His father stopped the car on the left side of the road and, in the sudden stillness of the world, with the roar of the car in their ears, they looked along the road they had come and ahead at the way they still had to go across the bridge. They were the only people in the whole world and this thought made Hama pity his father, and then ashamed to be ashamed of his father. His father pulled out the paper bag with their lunch and said: 'Let's find a cool place where we can sit.'

The grass-grown banks of the river were far back now from the water which flowed in a very thin trickle over a bed of pebbles.

Father and son walked slowly in the hot foot-sinking white sand along the river. There were tufts of water-gathered flotsam and river-dirt caught in the shrubs and boulders along the sand; and farther out from the banks, marking the extent of the floods that year. Half-buried in the sand and in the bed of the river Hama found some shells and up on the banks, in the trees, they surprised birds at sleep from the heat of the day.

They chose a water-polished rock in the shade of a *muonde* tree that grew on the very edge of a pool whose bottom they could not see. Water flowed smoothly and quietly round the rocks and boulders in the river and there were white bird-droppings on the rocks. It was very cool on the river. Hama leaned against the white and grey mottled bole of the tree and felt the tiredness leave him. It was as if that particular tree had been chosen in all the world for his back to lean on. A strange elation came upon him, but this turned into a sad melancholy when he looked at his father. The still day, the vastness of the blue sky and the strange loneliness of the river made him feel helpless. His father, too, looked very small – afraid of something both of them could feel but couldn't see.

All of a sudden, Hama was very afraid. 'We aren't going home to anyone's death, are we?' The lonely land, the river and the faraway sky forced him to talk in a whisper.

'I told you long back that we aren't going home to anyone's death and now just shut up, will you?' his father said. Hama felt that his father's agitation was not justified and something settled in him: an unknown fear. He felt, for the first time in his life, a deep need to appeal to someone for help. He saw his father's hands shaking as he tried to open the bag. The flesh on his face had become more wrinkled and his adam's apple was moving up and down as if he was having difficulty in swallowing something too big for his throat. His father now looked at the opposite bank of the river, very far away. Later, after some introductory coughs and shufflings in the bag, Hama heard him say:

'Feel hungry?'

The softness of the voice surprised Hama – and confused him. He didn't know whether the feeling of emptiness inside him was hunger or not. He nodded, though he didn't have any appetite for anything.

His father laid out several packages wrapped up in oil paper on the rock. He slowly began to unwrap them and laid out their lunch on the rock between them. There was bread cut into thin slices with wedges of cheese between the slices, pieces of biltong and two egg-rolls and a bottle of orange juice. They ate slowly, sipping in turn from the bottle, leaning against the tree. It was the first meal that Hama had ever had with his father and he couldn't enjoy it. He noticed that his father felt the same, too; he would take a timid bite on the bread, deliberate over chewing it, then, not looking at the boy, his hand shaking, reach for the bottle of the juice, and when their fingers touched in passing the bottle both of them felt like saying 'Sorry' –

then his father would swallow his food making a gurgle down his throat as if he were swallowing something hard and bitter, like medicine.

Then, all of a sudden, after the third bite on his second slice of bread, his father stood up and flung the unfinished piece of bread onto the water and walked a little way along the sand as if he were looking for something. Hama saw him wipe his forehead thrice and, there, dwarfed by the huge red bank, the white expanse of the heat-tormented sand and the great arid space above them, he looked forlornly small. Hama looked away and stared listlessly down the river at the smooth pebbles.

A bird screeched in the hot stillness and the boy nearly fell off the rock into the water. He had forgotten about the childhood stories of certain bird-cries that were portents of ill-omen. Now, the only bird of this type that he remembered was the owl. For two days an owl had cried on the roof of their house out in the reserve and Aunt Rudo hadn't said anything but he knew from the way her face fell that she felt that there was something bad that was going to happen. And there had been the accident.

And now, Hama wondered about this bird that had screeched up there in the trees on the bank. This bird wasn't an owl, he could tell that from its cry. Also, an owl was much bigger and slower in flight than this bird which he had not quite seen but only as a small fast dart against the glare of the sun above those trees on the bank. Maybe there was a bird fight up there. He saw some feathers dropping slowly down to the sand, descending in a spiral. The cry, so lonely, the black dart against the sun, and now the feathers – Hama felt afraid. But then the only other bird he knew that had the size of this other one was the honey-bird. The honey-bird was unpredictable. It could as easily lead you to a beehive as to a snake's nest. Hama shivered. He had once stepped on a coiled snake . . . oh. He instinctively recoiled from the horror and as he leaned forward from the tree he felt a soft brush on his neck and he fell off the rock with a scream into the water. He had the hiccuping sensation of hitting cold water and the sudden desperate blacking-out feeling of sinking fast beyond all help, and then the relief – the shocked jolt of hitting a shallow bottom.

The water barely rose to his waist.

Crouching in the water, he had a glimpse of his father's horror-mottled face and in his trembling left hand a yellow scarf and in the right a big open knife . . . Then quickly, he felt himself being pulled up the chilly slimy face of the rock, his metal leg banging against the face of the rock as he went up. His father's face was twisted up painfully and his eyes jumped and his whiskers trembled as he said: 'All right? You aren't hurt are you?' And his father's hands all over his body, quick and agitated, feeling for any broken bones. He even touched the metal leg. Hama felt so embarrassed with this unusual nearness and attention of his father's that he couldn't look him in the face, his body tensed *away* from his father. Then he felt really bad when he discovered that his father's teeth were all black with rot – some, rusty-coloured – and they gave off a very sickening stench. An unbearable sadness washed over Hama. He said: 'You scared me!' His father said nothing. He kept on feeling here and there, jogging the boy's arm or leg this way and that, making such a short-breath fuss over him that for a moment Hama looked very closely, keenly, at his father, a new but short-lived fear taking a grip on him. This feeling disappeared as quickly as it had come and Hama felt hollow inside and now he was looking at his father and wondering what he wanted a yellow scarf and such a big knife for. His father caught him staring, and in a sudden burst of emotion, he hugged the boy so hard, his body shaking so violently that all the breath left Hama. His eyes were tightly shut: Hama's eyes were turned on the knife.

Yes. It was a big knife. Pocket-size, but still big. It evoked a strange fear in him and then something in him happened and he felt very, very sad for his father. The thought came to him that this knife was too big and clumsy to pare one's fingernails with – because it just came to him that must be what his father needed the knife for – to pare his fingernails with.

'Why didn't you ask me for a razor-blade?' Hama asked, suddenly

90

wanting to help his father, fumbling in his wet pockets. He always kept bits of broken razor-blade in case he wanted to sharpen a stick to pick his teeth. It was a strangely pleasant sensation to lodge his tongue into some hollow in between his teeth and taste his own blood . . .

He found the blade and handed it to his father. Their eyes met. For a brief moment they both looked at the blade, then something violent seemed to happen inside his father. He closed his eyes tightly shut and with a pained cry grabbed the blade from the boy and flung it together with the knife far out across the water. Hama gasped as his eyes followed the course of the knife which flashed once in the sun and with a sad splash fell into the water, out of reach, of his life forever. He would have loved to own that knife . . . such a fine knife . . . He turned suddenly on his father and said: 'Why did you . . .?' His father slapped him hard across the cheek and then prevented his fall by quickly pulling him to himself and hugging him again, this time so tight that he let go when he heard Hama gasp in pain. Then his father was madly tearing the scarf into thin shreds and flinging them out into the water. His eyes didn't jump any more. They were narrowed on what he was doing. Hama was afraid. He turned away from his father to look at the pieces of cloth as they floated down the river. Then, behind him he heard big sobs. His father's head was dropped and he was crying into his hands. The first time to see his father crying, Hama was confused, then sad, then confused again and out of a need to appeal to someone – feeling very lonely and lost – he stretched out a hand and touched his father's hands which were cupped over his face. He tried to ply the fingers loose, to make his father uncover his face, and, finding the fingers too strong for him, he bit his lip, turned away and stared at the spot where the knife had fallen into the river. There was an itch in his nostrils, he felt them begin to flare, bit his lip harder – but there were tiny beady droplets in his eyes that split his vision into several bits – all complete in themselves – like seeing one image reflected in several mirrors – distorted. It was only by a very strong application of the will that he stopped the tears. Not a single drop touched his cheek. And his thoughts stayed on that one spot where the

91

knife had 'died', re-creating the whirlpools, following the path of the knife as it went down, he felt a calm come over him, a clean sad sort of job that made him aware, almost physically – although he wasn't touching him – of the human presence of his father. But something told him that it wasn't yet time to look at his father, so, he kept on looking down the river. Caught in a cleft made by two rocks, dancing slowly in the current, Hama saw the piece of bread his father had thrown away.

'Let's go,' his father said. Slowly Hama turned and saw his father's hand in mid-motion to touching his shoulder. He saw the hand drop, but the face took a longer time turning the other way. His father's eyes didn't jump much anymore, although they seemed to be looking into a very, very long distance.

★ ★ ★

They walked back to the car and the boy felt the warm trickles of water coursing down his back from his hair. His father turned the car's nose back the way they had come.

'We aren't going home?'

'Oh, yes we are!' his father said. But they were driving to Harare. Hama looked at his father. His father noticed it and making a large sweep of the land they were driving in, with his eyes, he said: 'My father – your grandfather – that is, used to spend days and days hunting in this area. This was before he settled where we are settled now. He was running away from some people – some enemies. Our home is really beyond those mountains.' For a brief second, his father's eyes rested on him, then they were looking at the land again. Finally they came to rest on the road ahead of them. Hama couldn't think of anything to say to this, so he kept quiet. The sun was almost down, not yet but going down, and his father's eyes were narrow points of light that distantly reflected the long road as it fanned into them. His father's eyes didn't jump about anymore.

'Think we can make it before sundown?' his father asked. 'I used

92

to, you know, when you were still a baby and I was driving for Makombe – but then that was a bus and it could take the punishment on these roads. Now, a small car like this – but, still, let's see . . . '

Then, all of a sudden, Hama lost the sound of the engine . . . only the rush of the cool wind and the roll of the wheels sitting firmly on the road. And all the way to Harare Hama listened to the roar of the car and his father's voice above the roar, relating what had happened in that dark time long ago before Hama had been born or was still a baby.

— 8 —

The Hero

Julius came out of the Staff Room. Behind him, as he went out, he was aware of the silent eyes of the Principal and the Headmaster. He walked with a defiant limp.

Everybody had gone to their classrooms for the last lesson of the day after the three-thirty break. The quadrangle was deserted. Bits of white broken paper lay scattered everywhere on the sand. Julius had the feeling of walking through a battlefield, looking at the dead bodies of the conquered. He felt contempt for all the conquered, whoever they were.

He walked straight to his classroom at the other end of Block A. He knew that more than three hundred pairs of eyes were looking at him from several windows. He could hear cheering hisses. But he did not care for them. He despised them all. He felt very tall. He suppressed an impulse to whistle.

Silence was shattered when he entered his classroom. The class teacher – who was also the Headmaster – was still in the Staff Room. The boys eagerly stood up and gathered round him. They fired barrels of questions at him. But he must not appear eager to answer them. . . A cynical lopsided grin hovered on his lips. He was disappointed that the girls did not rush to him as the boys had done but he was pleased to see that all their starry eyes, especially Dora's – his lovely deskmate's – were on him. He knew they must know all the details by now and be anxious to hear the end of it. But he would not give it to them yet. He must be cruel to himself. He must not care about what happened to

94

himself. They must see him as he truly was. They must completely forget all the impressions they had gathered about him on the football field or on the race track. He felt a savage desire to avenge himself on them, to see them wince with pain as they took the blow that was the real Julius. . .

'Oh, there's nothing to tell,' he said with a non-committal sneer. Then quickly he told himself that he must not look serious because, when they discovered the truth, they might think he was crying for himself. What he did not want from anybody was pity. He was a hero and heroes are to be admired not pitied.

'They just told me to go home and never come back.'

There was a stunned silence in the classroom. Julius noticed a crumbled look come on to Dora's face and quickly said, 'Oh, it's only a joke.' And there were sighs of relief and everybody was laughing with him, saying what a time he had given the Old Bat and what a stand he, Julius, had made. Julius felt very important. He felt a secret elation for they did not yet know the truth. Once they knew that he was really going home he was certain their admiration for him would be so strong that most of them would cry. He laughed carelessly. He had never felt this way before. He made a very poor joke and everybody laughed. In his heart Julius had always felt that he would do something that would make everybody envy him. And this was his day. He remembered his anguish on the football field and on the race track. . . Oh, he had known he would square up with them some-where, some time.

He said nothing more. He pretended not to hear his classmates talking about him as he took his books out of his desk and, after a dashing grin meant for an 'Excuse me', piled them on Dora's. He was whistling a very low tune which he knew only Dora could hear. She had once told him that she loved to hear him sing it. But he must not appear as if he was doing it for her. He must be indifferent, cruel. He knew she loved him but he must not be won so easily. He must torture her with love. . .

She could not help but see who he was now. He was not one of them. He led his own mysterious life. Mystery and danger, the key words. He was unique. He saw all the girls despising their boyfriends, throwing them away, for him. . .

He could still feel the waves of ecstasy his speech to the Principal and the Headmaster had set in motion in him.

'. . . I am not going to eat what you yourself would not willingly throw to your dog. I pay for the food here and I must have my money's worth. For a long time we have complained about the poor diet at this school, but you have plugged your ears with sealing wax. We have told your yellow prefects over and over. . . ' It had been a bold speech, a dangerous speech, and no one could have made it except himself, Julius.

Dangerous . . . He was going home because he was a dangerous element in the school, the Principal had said. And, thinking of the Principal, Julius felt a warmth for the Old Man. He knew that inwardly the Principal admired his courage. He had seen the Old Man shake his head with a smile, after that speech, and look at him with such an eye as if to say, 'You will go far, my boy', and Julius had known that it was only to please the Old Bat that the Old Man was sending him home. After all, it was the Old Man himself who had nicknamed Julius Little Caesar. Julius felt sorry for the Principal because he was about to lose such a fine young man. . .

Suddenly the Headmaster came in. He looked at his watch and said, 'All right, Julius. The ten minutes is up. Time for you to leave this holy place.' The Old Bat was in a joking mood but nobody joined him. All of a sudden everybody hated him. Julius was aware of the silent anger of his classmates against the Old Bat. He could hear rumblings and grumblings at the back of the classroom. And once again he felt very tall and so lightheaded that he nearly cried for love of all his classmates, and he was not angry with the Old Bat, but only sorry for him. But he was a hero. He must put on a show of resistance or something of that sort. . .

'Okay, okay, Bwana!' and giving a hollow, bitter laugh that sounded false rather than defiant he began to whistle . . . and from the corner of his eye he could see that Dora's eyes were very dark and tears glittered in them. . .

His heart pounding heavily with love, Julius was led out of the classroom. The Headmaster told the head boy of the school to take Julius to the dormitories and supervise his packing. And, hands thrust deep in his pockets, Julius walked tall between the two blocks of classrooms, three hundred pairs of eyes on him. He was going to pack and go. . . He was a dangerous element in the school . . . He had made a shocking speech. . . Julius could see Dora shedding a tear or two.

Later, he was standing on a little rise of the very long road to his home. He held his untidy little bundle of clothes in his right hand and with the left he shaded his eyes from the sun as he looked along that road. He felt as bad as when he had missed a ball on the football field. What he had done he felt, had been very childish. It was not as big as he had thought. He had achieved nothing. He saw Dora's look as he had left the classroom – he had lost her too. Now somebody else was going to take her. She would not care about him now. He felt something catch in his throat. Everything lost colour. His speech had not been so wonderful after all, and he wasn't so dangerous either; the look in Dora's eyes had not been of love nor admiration but of pity. Only the last words the Old Bat had spoken to him seemed true. He was 'a poor, spoilt, blind child who needed a loving mother's care'. Julius felt very sorry for himself. Already he could hear his step-mother's bick-bickering voice. . . He felt very tired, and from this little rise of the road, he could see the whole country lying flat and desolate and its lonely black immensity chilled him. He felt very small, very insignificant, and nobody cared what happened to him. The only important things to him now were that he was going home and the sun was setting and he was alone and it was sixty miles home . . .

Thinking of the untravelled journey in front of him, he made a loud statement in the Past Third Person Singular: 'The only time he has ever been happy was when he was at school.' And after saying this, he could not help the tears that came into his eyes.

9

The Setting Sun
and the Rolling World

Old Musoni raised his dusty eyes from his hoe and the unchanging stony earth he had been tilling and peered into the sky. The white speck whose sound had disturbed his work and thoughts was far out at the edge of the yellow sky, near the horizon. Then it disappeared quickly over the southern rim of the sky and he shook his head. He looked to the west. Soon the sun would go down. He looked over the sunblasted land and saw the shadows creeping east, blearer and taller with every moment that the sun shed each of its rays. Unconsciously wishing for rain and relief, he bent down again to his work and did not see his son, Nhamo, approaching.

Nhamo crouched in the dust near his father and greeted him. The old man half raised his back, leaning against his hoe, and said what had been bothering him all day long.

'You haven't changed your mind?'

'No, father.'

There was a moment of silence. Old Musoni scraped earth off his hoe.

'Have you thought about this, son?'

'For weeks, father.'

'And you think that's the only way?'

'There is no other way.'

The old man felt himself getting angry again. But this would be the last day he would talk to his son. If his son was going away, he must not be angry. It would be equal to a curse. He himself had taken chances before, in his own time, but he felt too much of a father. He had worked and slaved for his family and the land had not betrayed him. He saw nothing now but disaster and death for his son out there in the world. Lions had long since vanished but he knew of worse animals of prey, animals that wore redder claws than the lion's, beasts that would not leave an unprotected homeless boy alone. He thought of the white metal bird and he felt remorse.

'Think again. You will end dead. Think again, of us, of your family. We have a home, poor though it is, but can you think of a day you have gone without?'

'I have thought everything over, father, I am convinced this is the only way out.'

'There is no only way out in the world. Except the way of the land, the way of the family.'

'The land is overworked and gives nothing now, father. And the family is almost broken up.'

The old man got angry. Yes, the land is useless. True, the family tree is uprooted and it dries in the sun. True, many things are happening that haven't happened before, that we did not think would happen, ever. But nothing is more certain to hold you together than the land and a home, a family. And where do you think you are going, a mere beardless kid with the milk not yet dry on your baby nose? What do you think you will do in the great treacherous world where men twice your age have gone and returned with their backs broken – if they returned at all? What do you know of life? What do you know of the false honey bird that leads you the whole day through the forest to a snake's nest? But all he said was: 'Look. What have you asked me and I have denied you? What, that I have, have I not given you for the asking?'

'All. You have given me all, father.' And here, too, the son felt hampered, patronized and his pent-up fury rolled through him. It showed on his face but stayed under control. You have given me damn all and nothing. You have sent me to school and told me the importance of education, and now you ask me to throw it on the rubbish heap and scrape for a living on this tired cold shell of the moon. You ask me to forget it and muck around in this slow dance of death with you. I have this one chance of making my own life, once in all eternity, and now you are jealous. You are afraid of your own death. It is, after all, your own death. I shall be around a while yet. I will make my way home if a home is what I need. I am armed more than you think and wiser than you can dream of. But all he said, too, was:

'Really, father, have no fear for me. I will be all right. Give me this chance. Release me from all obligations and pray for me.'

There was a spark in the old man's eyes at these words of his son. But just as dust quickly settles over a glittering pebble revealed by the hoe, so a murkiness hid the gleam in the old man's eye. Words are handles made to the smith's fancy and are liable to break under stress. They are too much fat on the hard unbreaking sinews of life.

'Do you know what you are doing, son?'

'Yes.'

'Do you know what you will be a day after you leave home?'

'Yes, father.'

'A homeless, nameless vagabond living on dust and rat's droppings, living on thank-yous, sleeping up a tree or down a ditch, in the rain, in the sun, in the cold, with nobody to see you, nobody to talk to, nobody at all to tell your dreams to. Do you know what it is to see your hopes come crashing down like an old house out of season and your dreams turning to ash and dung without a tang of salt in your skull? Do you know what it is to live without a single hope of ever seeing good in your own lifetime?' And to himself: Do you know, young bright ambitious son of my loins, the ruins of time and the pains of old age? Do you know how to live beyond a dream, a hope, a faith? Have you seen black despair, my son?

'I know it, father. I know enough to start on. The rest I shall learn as I go on. Maybe I shall learn to come back.'

The old man looked at him and felt: Come back where? Nobody comes back to ruins. You will go on, son. Something you don't know

100

will drive you on along deserted plains, past ruins and more ruins, on and on until there is only one ruin left: yourself. You will break down, without tears, son. You are human, too. Learn to the *haya* – the rain bird, and heed its warning of coming storm: plough no more, it says. And what happens if the storm catches you far, far out on the treeless plain? What, then, my son?

But he was tired. They had taken over two months discussing all this. Going over the same ground like animals at a drinking place until, like animals, they had driven the water far deep into the stony earth, until they had sapped all the blood out of life and turned it into a grim skeleton, and now they were creating a stampede on the dust, grovelling for water. Mere thoughts. Mere words. And what are words? Trying to grow a fruit tree in the wilderness.

'Go son, with my blessings. I give you nothing. And when you remember what I am saying you will come back. The land is still yours. As long as I am alive you will find a home waiting for you.'

'Thank you, father.'

'Before you go, see Chiremba. You are going out into the world. You need something to strengthen yourself. Tell him I shall pay him. Have a good journey, son.'

'Thank you, father.'

Nhamo smiled and felt a great love for his father. But there were things that belonged to his old world that were just lots of humbug on the mind, empty load, useless scrap. He would go to Chiremba but he would burn the charms as soon as he was away from home and its sickening environment. A man stands on his feet and guts. Charms were for you – so was God, though much later. But for us now the world is godless, no charms will work. All that is just the opium you take in the dark in the hope of a light. You don't need that now. You strike a match for a light. Nhamo laughed.

He could be so easily light-hearted. Now his brain worked with a fury only known to visionaries. The psychological ties were now broken, only the biological tied him to his father. He was free. He too remembered the aeroplane which his father had seen just before their talk. Space had no bounds and no ties. Floating laws ruled the darkness and he would float with the fiery balls. He was the sun, burning itself out every second and shedding tons of energy which it held in its power, giving it the thrust to drag its brood wherever it wanted to. This was the law that held him. The mystery that his father and ancestors had failed to grasp and which had caused their being wiped off the face of the earth. This thinking reached such a pitch that he began to sing, imitating as intimately as he could Satchmo's voice: 'What a wonderful world.' It was Satchmo's voice that he turned to when he felt buoyant.

Old Musoni did not look at his son as he left him. Already, his mind was trying to focus at some point in the dark unforeseeable future. Many things could happen and while he still breathed he would see that nothing terribly painful happened to his family, especially to his stubborn last born, Nhamo. Tomorrow, before sunrise, he would go to see Chiremba and ask him to throw bones over the future of his son. And if there were a couple of ancestors who needed appeasement, he would do it while he was still around.

He noticed that the sun was going down and he scraped the earth off his hoe.

The sun was sinking slowly, bloody red, blunting and blurring all the objects that had looked sharp in the light of day. Soon a chilly wind would blow over the land and the cold cloudless sky would send down beads of frost like white ants over the unprotected land.

—10—

The Lift

When they were tired of going round the factories and shops in search of jobs, the boys went to the tall buildings at the heart of the city for their daily free ride in the lifts. It was the only fun they had and it made them forget a little their burning bellies and tired feet.

There were lots of clouds flung about the sky like cotton balls in a field. It was rather chilly and the boys felt sharply the pleasant warmth of the sun when it came out of the clouds, and both of them unconsciously looked up irritably when it darted behind another cloud.

At present, their minds, usually the colour of the changing streets and just as desolate, were fixed on the ride in the lifts.

Pearl Assurance Building, one of the tallest buildings in the city, had a guard at the wide entrance.

'Can I help you?' the guard asked.

'We would like to go up.'

'Floor?'

'Tenth.'

'What for?'

The boys looked at each other and hazarded an answer.

'We are doing correspondence courses.'

The guard looked at them suspiciously and then dismissed them with a flick of the hand.

'You are not allowed up there.'

The boys looked at the guard as if they had not heard him. Then their eyes turned to gaze at the wall above the lift where numbers went on and off in amber to show the lift coming down.

'There has been much stealing up there lately,' the guard said.

'We are not thieves.'

The guard's eyes swept over their heads and he dismissed them from his attention.

'Go away, boys.'

The boys turned to go. They passed two European boys of their own age. Looking back, the boys saw the guard take off his cap to the Europeans who did not answer him and quickly entered the lift and disappeared.

'Why did you allow those two to go up?'

'*You* are not allowed up there.'

The boys went out on to the street. It was not yet noon and they had nowhere to go and nothing to do to kill the time until night when they would go home to sleep.

'Wish I had kept that shilling after all,' one of them, thinner than the other, said.

'We had to have something to eat.'

'All the same, we could have used it now. It's so much nicer to have something to eat when you don't have anything to do.'

They were moving towards Salisbury Park. They had not talked of the park yet both of them knew that that was the only place left to go and rest.

'I was a fool to use that shilling,' the thin one said again.

His friend didn't answer because he always felt irritated by his companion's mourning for things that could have been. He felt like shouting at him to stop it but he controlled himself. He didn't care for words when he was tired. They made him even more tired than he really was.

'This is unbearable,' the thin one said once more.

But his friend kept quiet. He was hungry and there was nowhere to get money from. The thin one looked at him, knew that he would be asked why he was looking at him, and kept quiet, knowing that this

104

would only lead to a quarrel. But all the same, it could have been so much better if his friend would talk, then he wouldn't have to think and feel that he was not wanted, so lonely and so hopeless. The park was almost deserted except for two or three people lying on the forbidden grass, asleep or pretending to be asleep.

The thin one said, 'They are going to start trouble with the authorities.'

His friend answered him this time. 'It's silly to forbid people from lying on the grass. What is it there for?'

'It's the rules.'

'To hell with the rules.'

They found a bench under some bamboos and sat down. Immediately they had sat down, the talkative one said, 'They are not allowed to lie on the grass.'

'You have said that already.'

The thin boy looked at his friend and said nothing more. His friend leaned back on the bench and closed his eyes, pretending to go to sleep but the other one knew that this was the cue for him to keep quiet. Both of them were under a strain. They wanted to be somewhere else; the swimming pool, the beer hall – anywhere where there were people and fun and a chance to forget themselves. But there was only the wide empty park and themselves. The sleepless one looked around the park. He tried to steady his thoughts on the flowers and the trees and the light in the leaves of the trees and the shadows of the trees on the grass and the tall buildings of the city beyond the trees and the immense space of sky above the city, but there was nowhere his thoughts could rest and he was forced to come back to himself. But he was tired of looking into himself, of asking himself why he was like this and not like that, tired of examining himself, of finding faults with himself, tired of judging and condemning himself. He was tired of the whole circling process of his thoughts, so tired that he wanted movement – any movement, to feel that he was going somewhere and not just stationary. The feeling of doing nothing, of being nothing, oppressed and frightened him. He must talk – at least: that gave him a sense of direction, a feeling of really moving towards something. But his friend would not talk.

'That guard was just a nuisance. We wanted nothing except a ride. Only one ride in the lift.'

His friend stirred impatiently and said, 'Perhaps he was right. Lift rides are so short anyway.'

'But sometimes you get off a lift and find the sun has set.'

'Why don't you try to get some sleep? The sun would set faster.'

'I can't sleep during the day.'

'Then shut up please and let me sleep.'

The thin boy watched his friend as he moved towards the further end of the bench after these words. He moved towards the other end and closed his eyes. But he opened them again, worried about the space between them and the empty space that had opened up in him on closing his eyes.

'Can't we do something?' he asked.

Without a word, his friend rose and walked away to another bench and sat down, staring through the trees across the park towards the city. The thin one stayed in his place and struggled to keep himself seated, afraid to stand up and follow his friend, afraid to make even the smallest movement with his body that he knew before he had made it would fall into the pattern of yesterday, today and of tomorrow. So he tried to hurry the night when the darkness would hold his thoughts together and he wouldn't be worried by the distance between their two benches, the space that isolated them; so that looking at the two of them from afar, he saw that they were not friends. Not quite friends.

———11———

The Ten Shillings

Two years of tramping had hardened Paul Masaga into a cynical sceptic about his ever finding a job. He viewed his case as if it were somebody else's, without interest, with a shrug of the shoulders. He never thought seriously that he would ever work. So he had gone to the interview without any hope of success. He went so that he would not waste his time later on telling himself: 'If I had gone it might have been different.'

He had had no illusions of better times to come. His heart had not beaten as it would have done two years ago when he was still new to the city. He had grown up since then. He knew about the Europeans. They were all alike in their dealings with the African. An African would do or was bloody lazy. That was that. If they knew anything about the emotional life of an African it was that he was unstable, a potential rapist and murderer. So he had gone only to save himself regrets later on.

He was tired. He did not care what kind of work he did now. Two years of walking up and down the city. Two years of being kicked here and there in the locations. Two years of begging for food. Two years of sleeping in the gutters and drainpipes. *Mararapaipi*, they called him in the locations, pipe-sleeper.

Any day was just like another. He had forgotten how to laugh. He avoided crowded places, afraid he might run into people from home or ex-schoolmates. He avoided places where they cooked food because he would only excite a hunger he would not be able to satisfy. He had lost his Junior Certificate. He had not meant to lose it but what difference did it make? It had been just a piece of paper like any other. It had failed to get him a job while he had it. In fact, it had fooled him about his true worth. In the beginning he had gone looking for a clerical job or any of these white-collar jobs because he had trusted the certificate. People had told him that a JC would have no trouble getting a job. He had believed them. He had been hopeful and overconfident that he held the open sesame to life. He had written letters home and to school telling relatives and friends that he was now in the city – as if that were an accomplishment in itself. City-awe. That had been his disease. It was the disease of any rural African. Until they had spent a week of city-walking, city-hunger and city-cruelty. It had been humiliating to discover that he was not the only JC in the city. He had seen many of them at the Labour Exchange in Cameron Street and most of them held grades better than his. It had depressed him at the start, but he had learned to accept it, as he had learned to accept many more situations in life. The thing to know was that a JC was not important. It was a mistake to have ever thought so. The price one paid for going to a missionary school with a motto and believing all that they told one. Education, Paul thought sardonically, it awes us as did the bicycle, the motorcar and the aeroplane. It is a Western thing and we throw away brother and sister for it but when it fails we are lost.

So he had not worried about his certificate getting lost. He had been thankful. It meant that he would not be tempted to pull it out next time they wanted somebody to work on the road and thus lose the job. He must forget that he was a JC. It used to embarrass him in the first days. He would approach those stuck-up gatekeepers who would ask him, 'What kind of job are you looking for?'

'A clerical job.'

'Oh, you educated boys! Everyone out of his mother's belly talks of being a clerk! Do you think Salisbury is run by an army of clerks? Why don't you be humble like me and go dig on the road?' They would gather round him and laugh.

It was much easier not to give any particulars about himself. He was a man looking for a job. While he had had shoes and decent trousers he had had confidence, but this had disappeared with the first nail in his now sole-less footwear and the first patch on the seat of his trousers. Decent clothes and the JC had put the burden of taking himself seriously on him.

Now, he was just anybody going for an interview.

They sat for the interview in a big tobacco shed rigged up for the moment as a classroom. There were fourteen of them. By their gloomy look of crushed bitter importance, he knew they were all JCs.

He came out first and got the job. The European who interviewed them said to him, 'You're going to start work on Monday. Be here at the office at seven sharp. I shall give you a letter to take to Mr Thomson.'

Paul guessed that Mr Thomson was the boss he was going to work for. The interview had been on a Friday. That Monday morning Paul came to collect the letter at the office.

'You'll find Mr Thomson in Number Four Shed.'

Paul took the letter to Mr Thomson – who immediately struck him as formidable. Paul could not think of anything to call him except a Rhodesian farmer. Mr Thomson was supervising a gang of workmen who were carrying tobacco bales to a truck waiting outside the shed.

'Excuse me . . . ' Paul said, extending the right hand with the letter.

'Yes? What do you want?' Mr Thomson turned towards Paul, annoyed. Paul saw the coarse open-air brick red face, the intimidating mossy-concrete-wall chest, and the hard, dusty-blue eyes under the wide-brimmed farmer hat with the lion-skin band round it.

'I was asked to give you this letter, sir,' Paul said, instinctively retreating.

Mr Thomson ignored the letter. 'Are you the bloke that's going to work with me?'

Paul did not quite catch the words and he brought his head forward and said, 'I beg your pardon, sir?'

Mr Thomson exploded. 'God! And a deaf one too! I said are you the bugger who is going to work for me?'

'I have been told to give you this letter, sir.'

'I'm not talking about your bloody letter. I can't read. All I want to know is whether you have come to work for me or not. A simple question. Can't you answer that?'

'I think I am the one, sir.'

'Haven't you been told?'

'I have been told, sir.'

'Then what the hell do you have to think for?'

'I thought. . . '

'Listen, chum,' A podgy index drummed Paul's chest. 'I don't want any bloody thinkers here. I want somebody to listen and obey orders and do what he's told. Don't tell me you think. I do all the thinking for all of you bunheads here and you listen and do, see? My, I think, I think. You think my ass.'

Mr Thomson turned away from him and walked towards a desk in a far corner of the shed. Paul remained standing where he was.

At his desk Mr Thomson bellowed across the shed, 'You ain't gonna stand there for all eternity, are you?'

Paul started quickly for the desk. He still held the letter in his hand. Mr Thomson pulled out a piece of paper and a pencil.

'Name?'

'Paul Masaga.'

'Worked in a tobacco-grading shed before?'

'No, sir.'

'Whaaat?'

'I haven't worked in. . . '

'Then what the devil have you come here for?' Mr Thomson banged the desk with his fist.

'I passed the interview, sir.'

'So, what's that to me? I don't give people interviews here. I give them work, work, work!'

'I have a JC, sir, and. . . '

110

'Listen, Mr Jay See. I said I want someone who knows tobacco-grading work. I should have said I wanted a JC if I had wanted that. Some people don't seem to listen. When did you leave school?'

'Two years ago.'

'What have you been doing since then?'

'I have been looking for a job.'

'Then if that's what you know why the hell don't you go on looking for a job? Come on, Jay See. Get out.'

'But . . . but. . . '

'Want me to throw you out?'

Paul turned and made for the door. He could hear Mr Thomson snorting behind him. At the door of the shed the workmen were in a group looking at him. He did not stop to answer their whispered questions.

He walked to the office. The European in the office looked up when Paul knocked at the door.

'Yes? Oh, it's you Paul. What is it now?'

'Mr Thomson said I am not experienced.'

'Balls! What's all this? He complains to me he wants people. I send him fifteen in a bloody week and he says they're not intelligent. Now I send him someone who is intelligent and he says he has no experience. Hell's teeth!'

The man lifted a phone and rang Mr Thomson.

'Mr Thomson? . . . Yes. Now, what's wrong with Paul? . . . Oh, but you didn't tell me. . . Yes. Aha. . . That's it, is it? Well, I'll be. . . ' He dropped the receiver on its cradle.

He looked at Paul and said, 'Well, Paul, I'm sorry for all this. I tried my best but . . . well, I just don't know what's wrong with him. You know, we have never had people like you working for us before and I was beginning to think that now we might see something done at last. But it seems I should have . . . well, I really am sorry, Paul. For your trouble. . . '

The man was handing him a ten-shilling note. Paul accepted the money and thanked the man and went out. He could not think clearly.

111

He was so used to Mr Thomson's type of settler that this other one came as a surprise to him and he did not know what to think.

He looked at the note. A crisp new note. The first he had owned in two years. He felt sad and generous. People cannot help being what they are, he said to himself. With tears of goodwill he forgave everybody for the misery in the world.

—12—

Coming of
the Dry Season

One Wednesday Moab Gwati received a letter from Rusape. His mother was seriously ill. He decided to wait till he got his pay on Friday: Saturday he would go home.

He had his pay on Friday afternoon, and, as always happened with his money when he had it, it seemed to fly in all directions.

That Friday night he got hopelessly drunk with a girl he had picked up in Mutanga's earlier in the evening. Her name was Chipo but he did not know it till Sunday. They slept together in his room till eight o'clock Saturday morning.

He was still drunk and, after a cold shower he took together with Chipo, he ordered two quarts of Castle lager to take with their breakfast of fried liver and eggs.

After breakfast, with five other friends they drank till they dropped unconscious and their friends dumped them on the bed.

Early Sunday morning they had a beer and breakfast. They stayed in bed all morning. Moab felt his head beginning to ache. He had no more money and he did not want Chipo to know it.

At two o'clock he accompanied her to the bus station. He gave her a shilling for bus fare and a two-shilling piece for the fine weekend and patted her back in farewell. She said she had never been so happy in all her life. She stood in the queue to get on to the bus to Mufakose. Moab left before the ticket checker punched her ticket. As he was going away, the bus Chipo had taken passed him. He heard her yell and saw her wave to him. But he did not wave back. The black mood was on him.

When he felt this way Moab would walk for miles completely blind. It started always at the same emotional point, when, after a good time and he had no more money, he saw a gnarled old woman, thin as a starved cow, with a weak, saliva-flecked mouth and trembling limbs; very small dark eyes in carven sockets – a monkey face – and on her spare body threadbare rags wound as on a scarecrow stick. He would hear over and over the small mousy voice that was full of tears and self-pity, the voice that was a protest: 'Zindoga mwana'ngu, remember where you come from.' A warning, a remonstrance, a curse and an epitaph. With it, he could never have a good time in peace. Guilt, frustration and fury ate at his nerves.

When he spent four years without employment she had almost died from despair. She had cooked beer to the ancestors and then he told her he was working. And her health had improved. He knew that she had stood on her thin little legs and danced the *mbavarira*, which is both a praise to the ancestors and a prayer for the dead. He knew she had burned good luck roots for him.

It seemed he could never do enough for her. He had sent her money and clothes and a hundred-pound bag of mealie meal with his first pay. After this he had promised himself he would send her some more money – which he had done – yet there seemed no end to the things she needed. Her voice asked for far more than he could give. She had said once, when he had let her come to the city, 'Couldn't you find work somewhere near me? You know it won't be long and as you are my first born you must know all that you must do for me – for your own good – before I am gone. When I am gone you won't ever set anything right by yourself.' There were many things wrong with the family, she had told him. And she had been glad that he was working now because he would be able to set them right and release her from bondage.

It had so depressed him that, wishing her gone, he had told her that one day he would take a leave and she would say all she wanted done and he would do it. He had told her to console herself and remember

114

that she would be always in his thoughts. She had cried, whether for joy or sorrow, he had not known. But her tears had stayed with him and a guilt – about what he could not say – had dogged him like his shadow.

He smelled a sudden familiar smell. Dry, harvest-time smoke of burning maize-leaves. A shiver. Across the vlei the sun danced on the late red rapoko heads which nodded in the slight wind. In a pond of rust-coloured water rice was turning yellow and grass rotting in the pond stank. There had been unusually heavy rains this year. It was still raining, even now, in April. Another shiver. Why it should remind him of his mother, now very ill – at death's door as the letter had said – he did not know. He walked along the vlei, at the edge of Highfield Village. When he thought he should turn back, he entered Highfield from the west, having left it from the east.

He walked round and round Highfield. Night caught him still on the streets. Soon people left for bed and the dogs began their restless barking that would end with the coming of day.

In the northern sky he saw the bright arc of light that was the city. It reminded him of a veld fire at home. Only there was not the familiar smell of burning grass. If there had been, he knew he would have cried.

He watched the dogs trotting, mating, overturning bins in search of leftovers, and relieving themselves on the streets. When he felt tired he went home.

The severe yellow light of his room, mixed with the strong smell of onions in dripping and rotting sofa sack-cloth brought before him a prison cell and his mother. She was there now, imprisoned by life, trapped by her conscience, holding on tight till he was there to leave whatever it was she wanted to leave him. Her little cell, probably.

But she would have to let go without him. He had no money now. It was all finished. He switched off the light and lay on the bed unable to sleep till the milkman's bell. Lying in bed he heard rain falling. Thinking of his mother and a childhood belief he thought:

Soft earth

Wide spade
Are good friends.

He was listless the whole of the next day, a sunny Monday. His boss told him to take aspirin and go to bed but he said he was all right. The boss, an understanding jovial man, had advised him not to take these weekends so severely.

Afraid of his yellow room, he slept at a friend's that night. On Tuesday, while walking to work, a bushy-tailed squirrel crossed and then recrossed his path. His heart sank. He asked for a sick leave that day and went home.

He found a telegram waiting for him next door where the postman had left it with his neighbours.

His mother had died on Saturday night.

Moab walked dazedly into his room. He sat in a chair and looked into a mean backyard of motorcar scraps and hen manure. He was thinking of nothing.

'Hello.'

It came weak and faraway as if it were his own mother's voice greeting him from the grave. He turned towards the bed.

Chipo lay naked under a pink sheet. She smiled at him. For a long time he looked at her, dumb.

'I came yesterday evening. Your door was unlocked. I waited for you all night. Where have you been?' She sounded exactly like his mother. He hated her.

'Why have you come here? What do you want with me?'

Chipo looked confused, as if she had found herself, by mistake, in the Gents.

'But . . . but . . . you slept with me.'

'So what's that? Haven't you slept with many others? Why do you come to me?'

'But you are different. Moab, I wish you would marry me. I ask for nothing else.'

She looked at him sadly and her mouth twisted as if she had a pain somewhere. 'I have been alone too long.'

116

Suddenly he felt helpless, trapped. He said weakly, 'I did not ask you to come back.'

'I know. I just came back. You were so kind to me.'

He wondered what he had done for her. She was talking like his mother, suffering and saying things he did not understand. Why must they receive something else from what he intended to give – and then come back later to ask him for more of what he did not know how to give? He despised her. She had come back only to complicate his world.

'I don't have any more money,' he said harshly. 'That's what you want, isn't it? I don't have even a penny.'

'I know that, Moab. I didn't come for your money. I have too much of that.'

'Then why did you come back? Your type always comes back for money!' He glared at her.

She looked at him and did not answer. Her mouth twisted again, and there was a whiff of dry season air in the room. Moab's eyes filled.

'Go back where you come from! I didn't call you here!'

He stood up and yanked the sheet off her. She gasped but did not scream. She covered her private parts and hastily put on her dress. Moab noticed that her body was pitifully thin and starved.

He slumped back into his chair.

When she had finished putting on her clothes she took her handbag from a peg above the bed. From it she took a purse. Tilting the purse towards the light, so that Moab saw the thick wad of pound notes in it, Chipo extracted a shilling and a two-shilling piece and slapped them on the table beside Moab's right elbow. Then quietly she went out of the room.

Alone, Moab stared at the three shillings on the table. The ragged figure of his mother moved into focus. He felt damned.

His hand reached down for the money. He looked at it, wondering whether he should throw it out of the window on to the scrap heap. His head tightened and untightened with indecision: unclean money. But he had not even a penny in his pocket.

117

And his cheeks burning with shame, he furtively put the money into his pocket. He stood up and flung himself on the bed. He cried for something that was not the death of his mother.

——13——

The Accident

A man carrying a packet of tomatoes was knocked down by a car as he was crossing Cripps Road. He travelled in the air for twenty feet before he dropped to the side of the road. No one actually saw him hit.

He fell on his left side and face and did not move. His thigh was broken and twisted under him so that the foot faced backwards. His left arm lay twisted under him and the right was flung out backwards, palm up, as if he was asking for something. His grey socks had holes in them through which his yellow toes showed. One shoe lay on its side near his head. A piece of soiled cardboard which had been used to plug a hole in the sole of the shoe hung out like a tired dog's tongue. Further down the road the other shoe sat on the road as if it wanted to go somewhere.

His khaki trousers had been ripped at the back and nobody minded his dirty underwear which was soaking with blood. Blood came out of his mouth in a thick trickle and made a dark puddle on the sand. The distended nostrils were choked with more blood. By the slow up and down movement of his humped body people knew he was still alive but was having difficulty in breathing.

The European from the car came striding up the road. People turned to look at him. They watched him bend over the victim, then without touching him, he straightened his back and wiped his face. People could not read his face. It was difficult to read European faces. But they all noticed that the man wiped his face although there was no sweat on it. They noticed that he was short, thickset, with a bullneck that supported a big head. They noticed that he had hair round the sides of his head and in front near the forehead but none on the top of his head. And the strands of hair in front were brushed back, to cover the bald crown maybe, but later, as the people watched, the straggly strands of hair fell over his face, leaving the top as bare and red as an overripe tomato. Later, too, they noticed that something in his temple vibrated, minutely, like the wing of a mosquito alighted on a glass pane.

But in his face they could not read anything. They felt he was indifferent. Then they began to talk, in tones of suppressed sorrow and anger, and this grew in volume and intensity as more people came and stood on both sides of the road.

Most people took one look at the victim, covered their faces with their hands and did not look again but waited to hear the story. Without being told they knew that the European had done it. He was alone there and it was logical that it should be him.

The European stood a few feet from the victim, surrounded by the crowd whose language he did not know but whose feeling he understood. He did not look at them. Once, he lifted his head, and above the people's heads, looked up Cripps Road in the direction of the town. The red stop glare a hundred yards up the road returned his stare. Slowly he lowered his head to its original position. Two minutes later, almost imperceptibly, his head turned again to look down the road. He saw more and more Africans coming. No Europeans. Three minutes later he brushed his brow with his fingers as if he had a headache. His left arm hung straight down his side, fingers clenched. Around him, the crowd thickened and the talk that he did not understand hissed on like steam under pressure.

Cars passed by, changing down to dead slow as they approached the crowd, and picking up brutal speed past the people. And always in those cars that passed the people would catch sight of the stiff-necked, ahead-looking head of some indifferent or frightened European. There was only one old European woman who put her hands to her face and the man who was driving with her put his arm around her shoulders.

African drivers stopped their cars a little way past the crowd and came back to look and ask questions and stare and condemn. Those of them who did not see the European at first would ask, 'Who did it?'

'That Boer.'

'Which is his car?'

'That one down the road, with the broken windscreen.'

'He did it on purpose. I saw it all. This man', pointing to the victim, 'stopped to let the car pass but the bloody baboon went out of his way to kill him.' The speaker was a young man in a straw hat who had come much later after the man had been hit.

An old woman said, 'That's why I said to my son, "You aren't going anywhere. You stay here in the reserve with me. Who is there to tell me when this happens?" No, my son stays at home.'

The youth in the straw hat said, 'The man was not in his way at all. He was just carrying his tomatoes home. His wife is probably wondering why he has delayed so.'

'Oh, they don't care.'

'The bloody beasts.'

There was a silence. A wind blew down the road. A piece of dirty newspaper glided with the faintest rustle along the tarmac. It was caught by the man's bleeding head. Another gust came again. The paper freed itself, left the man, and glided further down the road. Past the crowd the paper rose into the air and sailed away over the Shawasha Men's Hostels to the west.

The man who said he had seen it all went on talking as if he was appealing to the people to do something. 'He was just standing beside the road not talking to anybody and this maniac comes along and knocks him down.'

The crowd was increasing. The European looked round and then walked down the road with short, nervous steps, his hands hanging by his sides. The people's eyes were on him all the way to his car.

'Is that him?'

'Yes. That's the murderer. I was standing talking to the man when

121

this – Boer knocked him down. I am going to say all I saw exactly as I saw it to the police.'

'They won't listen to you.'

'But I shall have said my share. I shall have shown them that they can't get away with everything here.'

'They have got away with much worse before.'

'But this time they won't.'

'They will. Until you rule them.'

'He wants to go away?' somebody asked, looking at the European who was now standing beside his car. They saw him look up and down the road, then bend into his car and search for something on the front seat. Nobody said anything. They just watched him with a silence that clearly said: You can't go away. The man straightened his back and blew his nose. Again he looked up and down the road. Then reluctantly he was heavy-stepping back to the dying man, adjusting sunglasses on his face. It was then that the people saw the mosquito-wing vibration in his temple.

There was a shrill shriek up the road. Heads turned.

'The police,' somebody whispered.

There was a slight backward-falling in the crowd, as the police landrover skidded to a dusty stop beside the dying man. Two policemen, a European and his African assistant, jumped out.

While the African constable pushed the crowd back on both sides of the road the European policeman studied the victim and wrote in a notebook. The other European moved nearer the policeman and looked on. Both of them were looking at the victim in silence. Then they were speaking in very low, almost friendly tones, the people thought.

'Blood is thicker than water,' somebody in the crowd said.

'Oh, they dare not let him go. I saw it all.' As if to confirm his statement the young man in the straw hat moved to the front line of the crowd, nearest the two Europeans and the victim.

'He did it on purpose!' the young man shouted for the benefit of the Europeans.

'Shut up, you!' The African constable glared at the youth. There was a sudden dangerous rumble in the crowd and somebody said, 'You don't drink with them. Remember that!'

The two Europeans did not turn their heads. The policeman went on taking notes while the other stared at the dying man and murmured something. The African constable moved round keeping the crowd well back from the road and the victim. He was not saying anything since somebody had told him to remember that he did not drink with the Europeans.

There was another shriek and, emergency light on the roof blipping, the ambulance stopped on the other side of the victim so that he was now between the two cars.

The white-coated driver jumped out, opened the back of the van and pulled out a stretcher. More people than were really necessary from the crowd stepped forward to help lift the man on to the stretcher and into the ambulance.

The two Europeans looked on, saying nothing. After the ambulance had driven off, they walked side by side down the road to the killer car. Then with the crowd's eyes on them, the Europeans walked back again to the police car.

The policeman spoke. 'Is there anyone who saw this man knocked down?'

The youth in the straw hat stepped forward, and without taking off his hat, said, 'I saw everything. I saw the man knocked down.'

'You sure?' the policeman asked, narrowing his eyes with a sideways glance at the African constable, who interpreted the question into vernacular.

'Sure I saw everything.' The youth's face showed no expression.

'All right. Stand there. Anybody else?' Again the African constable translated and added that nobody should step forward who had not seen the man actually hit. There were derisive rumbles from the crowd and two other young men defiantly stepped forward. It looked as if more were prepared to hand themselves over but the constable held up his hand and said, 'Enough.'

'You saw the man knocked down?'

'Yes, Nkosi.'

'Are you sure?'

'Yes, Baas.'

'Good. You will give your names to constable Tayengwa and you will come with us for a statement at the police station.'

'Yes, sir.'

After the witnesses' names had been taken the police car drove off, followed by the killer car.

When they had gone there was a silence in the crowd, a disappointed silence.

'He's going to be released.'

'But those three men have courage. If only we had ten more like them – men who can stand up and tell them that they are wrong.'

'It will be a long, long time before we have ten like that.'

'We have them, only. . . ' And arguing sad politics the crowd dispersed, all going in the same direction, south-west, into the location. They all felt the same thing: once again, nothing has happened.

14

Some Kinds of Wounds

Kute pushed the woman gently into the room and before she could sit down on the floor – as I saw she was about to – I quickly offered her a chair. Suddenly the smell of the room changed. The woman carefully sat on the edge of the chair, her hands in her lap, eyes cast down. Kute remained standing in the doorway.

'Okay?' he whispered.

'It's all right,' I said.

'Good. Won't be long. A minute to work the windowpane loose – and – halleluya!' He was in sudden good spirits.

'Mind the good neighbours,' I warned him.

'They call me Cool Cat Kute. And anyway who would hear a thing with that kind of roof-wrecking racket going on? Tell me Gatsi. How did I go and choose myself a father like that?'

'The ways of the Almighty are mysterious and not to be sniffed at with our clay snouts,' I offered him the wisdom of our seven-month friendship.

'Amen. Could we borrow a knife?'

I handed him my all-purpose table knife. 'Mind you don't break it. It's the last of its kind in this country.'

'Priceless, to be precise,' he said, giving it the expert butcher's professional squint. 'It's in safe hands.' Turning to the woman, he whispered loudly, 'Patience. The Reverend Gatsi here will take good care of you. I lost my key and the spare is opening some bright future for me in my father's dreams,' he said this last bit nodding towards the sound coming from his father's room down the corridor.

The woman didn't say a thing. He went out to the back where the door to his room was. The smell in the room was growing thicker. I guiltily looked at the window and saw that it was partly open. I couldn't bring myself to open it wider.

Slowly I turned my head towards the woman. She wore a sleeveless top of some faded, very thin pink material that showed she had nothing to hold up her breasts. She had on a homemade black skirt and her dusty feet were covered by worn-out once-white tennis shoes without laces. Her head was covered in a headcloth that hid almost half her face down to the top of the bridge of her nose so that her eyes were in shadow. It gave her a very mysterious look which I was sure must have appealed to Kute's sense of the sensuous. There were deep lines down from the flanks of her nostrils to the corners of her mouth. These lines gave her an old woman's face although I could sense that she was far from being old. In fact, there was a certain subtle awkwardness in her that made me feel she wasn't even aware that she was a woman.

She looked as if she had come a very long way on foot. She looked that dusty and travel-used – a kind of slept-in-everyplace air about her. And she sat in that chair as if she couldn't trust herself to let go and relax, as if she knew that was only a temporary resting place on the long road. And yet, in spite of all this, there was a kind of watchful-stillness about her, a kind of relaxation-in-motion that made me feel that she was as much at home in that chair as on her feet or asleep. Walking, sitting or sleeping, her body had erased all the differences and acquired its own kind of separate peace with her mind.

She didn't look at the pot of sadza cooking on the fire, nor round this room which must only have been strange to her with the numerous books piled knee-high against one wall, some cheap reproductions of some abstract paintings, the typewriter, the single un-made bed and the clothes hanging from wire-hangers in a corner. She did not even look at me or at anything else except at her hands in her lap. I wondered whether she even saw those hands. The *silence* in her

126

resting hands suggested some deep religious experience in her. Those hands – which were clearly not sweating from nervousness as mine would in the presence of strange people or unfamiliar rooms – gave me a feeling I had never had since coming to the city some ten or so years back. They belonged to the depths of the heart of the country and all that I missed. She reminded me of where I came from and suddenly the smell in the room was clearly a mixture of human sweat and soil and grass and leaves as we carted hay for the cattle. Once I knew what it was, I felt at home in it.

Outside, I heard the scraping of the knife on Kute's window.

'He has lost his key and he is trying to remove the windowpane so that you can get in,' I told the woman, for something to say.

She didn't say anything. Suddenly, I felt as if she were accusing me of something. I turned the stove low. I had lost all appetite. Then, remembering home, I felt guilty all over again. I had lost the rural sense of hospitality and she would never forget how I had received her in my house.

'Want anything to eat?' I asked her, trying to cover up. And that was wrong too. You don't ask strangers who come into your house whether they would like food or water. You give them what you have and leave them to say no or to eat.

'I am all right,' she said.

'Honestly, I mean – it won't take long –'

'Don't worry, brother.' Her mouth gave the faintest suggestion of a smile and she left me to stew in my own guilt.

I took up a novel and tried to read. I read one line three times.

'Where do you come from?' I asked.

'Mount Darwin. Chesa.'

I put the book face down on the table and stood up to look out through the window. Behind me I could feel that she wasn't even taking advantage of this to look at me. I sat down in the chair and picked up the book again.

After some time the woman spoke, 'He told me this is his house.'

'It's his father's and he is the first born, so I suppose that makes it his.' She didn't seem to have heard me. I said, 'But his father sleeps in his own room and Kute has his own at the back.'

'And you are his brother?' she asked with the slightest hint at raising her eyes.

'I am only their lodger.' She didn't seem to understand that. 'I pay rent to them for this room. We are not related at all.'

She didn't say anything to this.

I picked up the book, decided that poetry would be easier in the circumstances. I threw the book on top of the pile of other books and pulled out a much-referred-to, dog-eared paper-back edition of Paul Celan's *Selected Poems*. His poetry was very difficult yet most of the poems were almost haiku-like in their brevity. I thought I would work on the meaning behind the verbal appearance while I waited for Kute. What bothered me was that the words were all quite simple – I didn't need a dictionary for their conventional meanings – yet the way they were used here was beyond me. Words.

'And his mother?' she startled me.

'His mother?'

'Your – your–'

I understood. 'She is keeping their home out in Manyene Reserve. She only comes to town for two weeks once every year.'

We fell silent. I returned to my poetry.

Later, 'Is he married?'

'No.'

Pause.

'Do you think he will let me sleep here tonight? Only for tonight?'

Down the corridor I heard the snoring reach such a pitch that it was impossible for it to go any higher.

'I don't know,' I said. 'He might.' But then you would have to leave at half-past four in the morning, I didn't tell her.

'It won't be long now,' she said. 'If he would only let me put up here for the night, tomorrow I am sure I shall be all right. I have got a friend in Highfield – that's what he said – Highfield. Do you know where Highfield is? This friend – I have known him for such a long

128

time and I know he wouldn't lie to me. Back home I . . . he . . . he said he would take me to Highfield.' Pause. 'Is it far from here, this Highfield?'

I could smell the sadza burning but I didn't have the energy to take the pot off the stove. I had turned the flame low thinking it wouldn't need attending to till the woman had left the room.

'Is it far?' she repeated.

'No,' I said, suddenly unforgivably angry with Kute. I wondered what he had told her and *how* she had got here without asking for directions.

'This friend of yours in Highfield,' I asked quickly, 'did he ask you to come to him? Wasn't he waiting for you at Musika Bus Terminus?'

She simply shook her head and said nothing. How the hell could I help her if she wasn't going to talk? I looked out through the window, seeing nothing, feeling a newer kind of chilly guilt creep over me. I was suddenly aware of the depth of my hatred for Kute but I couldn't do anything and just sat there feeling as if I were keeping vigil in a house of mourning.

'When he left there was no time to say goodbye,' she startled me once more. I turned towards her.

'My boyfriend,' she helped me although I was sure she could not have read my thoughts. 'I didn't even see him. He left word with one of his friends to tell me that should I ever come to Harare I should look him up in Highfield.'

'And the number? Where exactly in Highfield were you to look him up?'

'There was no time,' she hadn't heard me or she was just dumb. 'They came for him the following morning but he had gone.'

I was trying very hard to settle in between the lines so I didn't say anything.

'They knew he often came to our place to see me. I am sure they knew he was going to marry me. They know everything out there. They thought I would try and hide him. I wasn't there when they came. They shot my mother and my father. I was at a friend's –

129

Chengeto – where I had put up for the night because of the curfew. Then we heard the shots and saw the flames and the smoke as our home burned down.'

'I am sorry,' I said and then felt very stupid. I was sinking.

'Chengeto's folks advised me to run away. Just as I was leaving I could see the dust of their cars making towards Chengeto's home.'

'Is it that bad out there?' What was I talking about? Or, rather, how do you – what do you say when someone tells you a story like that?

She looked up at me. Her eyes seemed to be points of light coming a long way through a tunnel. 'If the soldiers suspect you of harbouring or giving food to *vanamukoma* they kill you. If *vanamukoma* suspect you of passing information to the soldiers, they kill you. If your neighbour hates you he can tell either the soldiers or *vanamukoma* that you are a sellout and either way you will be killed.' She lowered her eyes. I would have felt easier had there been any kind of self-pity or suffering in her voice.

'So, what did your boyfriend do? Why did they come for him?' I felt it wouldn't be safe for me to ask her *who* came for him.

'Nothing,' she said. 'He didn't do anything at all. The soldiers just don't feel happy with a young man of twenty doing nothing out there.'

'But are you sure that he came here when he ran away?' I felt that it was more likely that he would want to join *vanamukoma* in the bush if the soldiers were after him. He would be safer in the bush.

'Wouldn't it have been safer for him to run into the bush?' I asked seeing that she didn't seem to have heard me.

'He was going to marry me when all this fighting was over,' she said, apparently not interested in my question. I felt like someone who had been invited to a party and then found himself ignored by the host. It made my guilty feeling more complex. I felt that she was silently asking me why I wasn't also out there? I looked at my pile of books and suddenly I wished I hadn't let her into the room.

'He was going to marry me,' she said. 'He would have married me if he hadn't felt that one day he might join the fighters – *vanamukoma*. He was quite friendly with them but they told him to help his old

130

people on the farm. They didn't even recruit him to be a *mujibha* – that's the name for their messengers or spies – local village boys who keep *vanamukoma* supplied with information.'

'I know,' I said and then wished I hadn't said it. The pinpoints of light from her dark tunnel bored into me but she quickly dropped her head.

I looked through the window. I felt ashamed of the poetry. What was Kute still doing? The scraping had stopped.

'It must be tough living out there,' I said, wanting to hear more. It was like a sore which you felt needed scratching.

'We no longer think about it.'

'What are you going to do if you don't find him here?'

She looked up at me, but not accusingly, rather pleadingly, as if asking how I could be so cruel – but then I might have been wrong in thinking so because nothing in her showed that she needed my pity. Instead, I could feel deeper silence settling in the room, that kind of silence one senses in places where a human life has been lost – the scene of an accident or some other disaster. A desperate, frightening silence that makes you ask metaphysical questions.

'How far is this Highfield?' she asked after some time.

I heard a tap on the window. I looked up and saw Kute looking in, grinning. I restrained myself from slapping that greedy, meaty grin off his face.

'It's open,' he said. He came round to the door and entered without knocking. He handed me the knife. 'Thanks, Gatsi,' he said. 'Keep it safe for future journeys to the land of milk and honey – it's an all-purpose Moses's rod,' he nodded towards his father's snoring, 'ask Pharaoh and the Red Sea.' He laughed and rubbed his hands.

I didn't look at him.

'Hey, what's going on in here? It's as if you had just buried a dearly beloved.'

I didn't answer him.

'All right, Reverend Gatsi. All right. Come on, sister.' He was angry.

131

They went out and Kute's anger reminded him to close the door softly. His father's snores were coming along the corridor like trapped wind in a tunnel. There were slight rustles and soft-footed thuds as they helped each other through the window into Kute's room. I sat in my chair, doing nothing.

Forty minutes later I heard a sound as if someone was crying. I listened hard and heard them coming out. Their shadows passed by my window and I heard their footfalls fade beyond the yard to get swallowed by other footfalls on the street.

Kute came back five minutes later. He entered my room without knocking.

'Silly bitch,' he said, sitting on the edge of the table. He wanted my compliments or some kind of comment that would make him feel good. He always felt he wasn't living until someone else told him so. When he saw that I wasn't going to answer him he went on, 'Thinks this is a home for the pregnant, destitute and aged.' He shook a cigarette out from my pack which was lying on the table and lit it. He drew in smoke and filled his cheeks and then blew it out stintingly, afraid to waste good smoke.

'Wanted to spend the night here. Wouldn't accept any money. And does she stink! If the old goat weren't around I would have asked her to have a bath first.'

'Where did you pick her from?' I asked.

'The pub.' He pulled on his cigarette and began to laugh. 'Can you imagine it, man. She was asking for directions to Highfield *in* Highfield! Must have got into town today. Didn't even go to school too. Can you imagine that – in this day and age?' He had a good laugh over that and went on, ' "Would you please tell me where Highfield is, brother." And I took her right to Highfield – here! I told her Highfield was too damn far to get there tonight.'

'Did she say what she was doing in the pub?'

'That's her problem. If I had known she was pregnant I wouldn't have bothered with her. Silly bitch.'

I was quiet for some time while he smoked and thought over the

132

wrong she had done him.

'Where have you taken her now?' I asked.

'I put her on the street and pointed east, south, north and west and told her this was all Highfield.' He laughed. The smoke caught in his throat and he coughed. 'You know Gatsi. I just don't understand these country women. I offered her money and she refused it. And yet any fool can see how desperately she needs food, decent clothes, and if she is going to have a baby – hell. Probably she will throw it down some sewer drain or dump it on some rubbish heap for the dogs.'

I looked through the window. 'Where did she go?' I asked.

'How the hell should I know? Does her type ever lack places to go to? She just walked straight away from me without looking back – as if she knew where she was going. How the hell would I know where she was heading?'

I didn't say anything.

'You know, I think she was after something more than money. You can never tell in these times. Telling me she has walked all the way from Chesa or whatever place she mentioned – after her parents had been killed and she escaped – who does she think will believe that baboon-and-hare story in these times? Does she look the type that could have walked from Chesa to you? The dirt, the stink and the simple mentality might belong to Chesa yes – but don't let that fool you. She could have run away from home in Mbare – her father after her with the old battleaxe for conceiving a bastard – and now she wants to con some fool of a man into keeping her till she delivered and later she will run away again with all his money and clothes and everything – leaving him to look after her bastard. Damn silly bitch!'

He smoked for some time in silence. I knew he was looking at me, waiting for me to say something like 'Good old Cool Cat Kute', so that he could really begin to purr, stroking his whiskers and licking his fur as if he had finally landed the record-breaking rat.

'Hey,' he said suspiciously, 'what's got into you?'

I didn't answer him.

'Well, I got what I wanted out of her – Chesa stink, rags and all –

133

and she can get what *she* wants from someone else. Saved me the trouble of scrounging for cigarette stubs though. Mighty considerate of her. *Kakara kununa hudya kamwe*, as the wise old folks had it. Dog eat dog.'

'Kute.'

'Yes?'

'You should have given her the money, you know. Forget about lying to her about Highfield. But the money, at least.'

'Well, she refused it, didn't she? You aren't suggesting that I should have gone down on my knees and begged her to take it, are you?'

'She is not your usual type. Probably she didn't know all you wanted out of her is only *that*.'

'Heey! come on, Gatsi. You know very well what she wanted – a good bed and a man for the night. Then tomorrow she would have come back again – and tomorrow and tomorrow till I was so entangled in her I wouldn't know whether my head comes before my arse or what.' He was now pleading with me. He didn't want me to get him wrong. He lived on the actor's habit, the clap of the hand and the cry for more.

I kept quiet and turned to look at him.

'Look,' he said. 'Why this sudden interest in that – that slut?'

'She is no slut. She may be pregnant but she is no slut.'

'Does she come from your home?'

'No.'

'Then?'

I didn't answer.

'Or you wanted her for yourself?' He had solved the problem for himself. He laughed long and hard. He patted me on the shoulder and laughed some more till tears stood in his eyes. 'Guts-less Gatsi! Why didn't you tell me you wanted her? I could have left her all to yourself and gone and found me another tail. Now you are growing up. You are coming to my way of thinking now. That's a good sign. The heavens augur well for a bumper crop in tail this year!' He looked at me as if I

134

were a long-lost brother suddenly come home without warning. 'Tell you what,' he said. 'When I make my patrol tomorrow we might go together, right? Good Gutsy Gatsi. Man does not live on books alone but on . . . '

'I think you should take it slow,' I cut into his sermon.

'Take what slow?'

'You know what I am talking about. Once or twice per week is all right. Not everyday.'

'What the hell are you talking about?'

I could see dark anger and fear gathering in his eyes like storm clouds.

'It isn't healthy you know.'

'What isn't healthy?' He was hedging, trying to avoid to face it. He knew what I was talking about.

'This won't get you anywhere, Kute.'

'The hell you say!' He banged the table with his fist. 'Has my old man asked you to interrogate me about this?'

'I don't need your old man to see that.'

'O, so you have decided to play saviour! With your kind of guts?' he sniggered. 'Look, you are just jealous, man. You can't do what I can do and you dream of doing it and when the moment of truth comes you haven't got the guts, right? You wanted that piece of tail and you hate my guts for doing what I have done to her. Why don't you ask me how it's done and I will give you a few elementary lessons, huh, Gatsi-boy?'

'That doesn't change the fact that you won't get anywhere. Look how many times you have been to the doctor. Your seat-hide must be as perforated as a sieve now. Sounding tough and brave doesn't get you anywhere either.'

'Hell, man, hell! And what has ever got me anywhere in this rotten world? Third division in Form Four and everyone at my neck saying I wasn't applying myself. Four years tramping round the country, knocking on every goddam door for *any* kind of job and being shooed off with a boot in my arse and at home my old man out for my scalp telling me I am not searching hard enough. I would have drunk, taken drugs – anything to jump out of my skin – but that stuff hasn't been good for me. And now you begrudge me the one and only little thing that keeps me going.'

As always, the anger was crumbling into his other only weapon that was even worse than the anger. It was as if I had taken the lid off a sewer-drain manhole knowing exactly what would come out but not quite prepared to take what finally came out of it.

'Listen,' I said, 'I am only trying to help.'

'Yeah? Give me a job then – and money and keep me sane.'

'You are getting more than enough money from your old man.'

'For my private studies. And he didn't give it to me until he saw you with all those books. He thinks it's the books that get one a job.'

'I don't see how else you want to get a better job if you aren't going to study for it.'

'So you haven't heard of the University blokes who have been years looking for jobs?'

'They are no reason why you shouldn't study yourself.'

'What the hell do you mean I am not studying?'

'Don't fool yourself, Kute. Since you bought those books you haven't touched a single one of them. If your old man had been to school he would know exactly what you are doing to him.'

He leaned towards me menacingly and hissed, 'You aren't going to let him hear that, are you?'

I said nothing.

'Well are you?' His nose was only a few inches from my face.

'It's your funeral, Kute,' I said, rising to close the window. 'But I wish you wouldn't take advantage of your old man in this way.'

He leaned back in his chair and brought his hands to face, sighed and looked blearily at me. He said, 'You don't know how it is.'

'I know.'

'No, you don't.'

We were quiet for some time.

'Know what,' he said. 'When I ran into you that day in town – must

136

be six months or so now – and you told me that you were looking for a room, you don't know how good I felt. To have someone – a classmate from way back those years in school – to talk to. Someone like you to confide in, someone who would understand. I knew I could trust you. You were one of those who always understood me. I felt good, I tell you. And the best feeling I ever had in my life was when I knew I could ask my old man – persuade him – to give you a room here. I knew he would know I was moving in good company. I knew he would know that I wasn't as useless as he seemed to think. That made me feel good, Gatsi. To be able to do something for someone, for nothing. I almost cried, Gatsi. It's a thing I have always wanted to do all my life but when you don't have what others have, how do you do it? Who will believe you are sincere? I know I don't have your kind of brains. Even in school, but should the luck always come to those who have brains alone? Look at me now, still at the bottom of my class while you are well tucked in in that firm of publishers. And my old man believes it's because I am lazy. Do you know that my old man loves you more than me – his own son? Do you know that?'

'No.'

'The hell you don't!'

'Listen Kute. I know how you feel. I have been through something like it too.'

'But not four years, man. Four years is too long for any man to be still hoping.'

'But you can't just give up like this. You aren't helping anyone, least of all yourself, by being bitter and attacking your father and dropping your studies and chasing tail. You have to face yourself, find what you want to do and do it.'

He squinted dangerously at me, 'So I was right, huh?'

'Right about what?'

'You are together with my old man. Shit, man. I thought you were my friend. I thought you understood. I persuaded my old man to give you a room here and now you are better than me – his own son!'

'Don't hang your own shortcomings round other people's necks, Kute.'

'Dang shortcomings! I know you have been stabbing me in the back since that time you started staying here. Neither you nor my old man has the guts to say it to my face but I know it. I have been too long among people to be fooled by toothpaste-advert smiles.'

'You are imagining things, Kute.'

'Exactly. And who taught you that word? Let me tell you. It's that pig gruntling down the corridor who would sell his own son for chicken shit.'

'You are frustrated, Kute and that's all. You can't face the real world that's doing this to you and so you turn against those that would –'

'You mean people like you? You are damn right. It's people like you who come messing up things for us unfortunates who should be shot.'

'You are not an unfortunate, Kute –'

'The hell I am not! When they have looked inside my head and decided that I am not good for nothing else and what kind of load do you think I always carry round with me if it isn't Maths-20%; English Lit.-15%; History-40%; Geography 19%? They have made my old man and all people I know believe it and now you are pushing it further into my old man's head that I am completely castrated with your books and studies. He really believes it's this shit you are doing in here that makes people and because I can't measure up to it – I am not his son any more. Do you realize what I am talking about, you squirty worm?'

'Listen. I just wanted to help. Forget all I said. I was just worried that you might catch it worse than what you are receiving treatments for right now.'

'Just like my father. Now you are the bigger brother that I don't have. Do you know what it feels like to be the big brother in a family of eight and never be able to help your little brothers and sisters just because you have been labelled incompetent by some smart Mr Know-it-all who has had the further luck of having it believed by your own family?'

'Then prove yourself!'

'Prove my death, you mean?'

'So you want to kill – you would rather kill yourself?'

'Who says I am killing myself?'

'How many times have you been to the doctor for the past half-year and he hasn't diagnosed VD in one form or another?'

'So you told my father that too? You are not leaving any stone unturned are you? You want to see me completely destroyed.' He put his hands to his face.

'How could I tell him *that*?'

'Sure you didn't when you shout it out like that as if you were the short-changed tenth wife in a polygamous marriage!'

'Kute.'

'Don't Kute me!'

'Listen.'

'Listen yourself, Mr Gutbug! It's me who feels the pricks of the doctor's needle. It's me who is going to do the dying if there is going to be any dying around here. And you won't hear me complaining when I am dead, hear that? Not a single word from me when I am down and under. I'll be so far away and out of it all that I won't bother you. Then you can continue with your books all year round, all your damn precious life. God, I wish I had never met you!'

I looked at him. There were pieces of broken glass in his eyes.

'Please leave me alone with my life, Gatsi, will you? I can't be as bright as you and you can't do what I can do although no one else thinks it's anything and when I die you will be king of the world and cock of the roost and I hope to honest God you drown in your own piss. So leave my goddam rotten life alone, will you!'

I looked at him and he turned his face away from me, swallowing hard. I looked through the window and saw only my reflection in the glasspane.

'Just stay out of my life,' he said, his eyes to the wall but his fists clenched so hard that several veins bulged out in his neck.

139

He stood up and, without looking at me, opened the door and went out, closing the door so silently that the echo of its eternal bang haunted me for the next three weeks as I tramped from one location to another in search of new lodgings. I had also given away the bulk of my books to friends, because I found that it was just too much useless baggage to lug around with me whenever there was a need to change lodgings.

—15—

The Victim

Rungano brought him into our little kitchen at the other end of the block just as I was about to have supper.

'What's wrong?' I was tired and didn't feel like talking to anyone then. It was seven o'clock and I could hear the men shouting in the big communal kitchen at the other end. I just wanted to be alone. I would be the last to go to bed around one o'clock in the morning but that didn't mean I needed anyone's company. I could sense that sometimes Rungano hated me for this but he wouldn't bring himself to say it to my face.

'Look at him,' Rungano said as if he were accusing me.

I straightened up from the steaming pots of sadza I had just taken off the stove.

The man's face was covered with blood. It was difficult in the guttering candle light to see where he had been hurt. By the size of his right eye, I could tell that it was swollen. I couldn't recall how his lips had looked before but I thought they were too fat to be normal for his usually thin face. There were minor cuts and bruises on his knees, elbows, arms and legs. He could have had a bad fall. The blood made his injuries appear worse than they really were. And the way he had walked in suggested that there might be some internal injuries as well.

I felt afraid and angry with Rungano for bringing the man to me.

'What happened?' I asked.

'Someone tried to kill him,' Rungano said.

'You are joking.' I couldn't believe him. I had heard people who got

141

killed but I hadn't seen one, dead, or just after escaping getting killed.

'Mr Moyo, I am dying,' the man said, 'I must see the manager at once.'

I stepped closer to him. I knew very little about wounds, blood or death. I always felt that they were something that would never happen to me. I was suddenly very frightened. Although I knew that the man was drunk, therefore likely to exaggerate things a little, I was frightened. I felt it was all my fault because I had sold him *nipa* earlier that evening. He and the other men now shouting and singing at the other end of the block had been drinking *nipa* which I had sold them down in the ravine below the Forestry Compound.

'What happened really?' I addressed Rungano who was leaning against the wall, his hands in his pockets.

'Ask him.'

'He tried to murder me,' the man said. He was sitting in the single chair in the room. He held his head in his blood-covered left hand. In the right hand he held his left gumboot. I couldn't see where the right boot was. He was barefoot.

'Who tried to murder you?'

'Samba.'

'Why?'

'He hates me.'

'But why would he want to kill you?'

'They all hate me here,' the man said. 'And I must see the manager at once.'

He held his right side and slid from the chair to the floor. He leaned his back against the wall and stretched out his legs.

I looked over at Rungano. He shrugged his shoulders and pulled out his cigarette pack.

'I wouldn't let him see the manager if I were you,' Rungano said, lighting a cigarette.

'I know. Maybe we should go and see Ngoro?'

'*Nipa* is illegal, you know,' Rungano said.

'I said I know.'

We were quiet for some time.

'I don't want to see anyone but the manager,' the man said. 'They all hate me here. I know they sent Samba to waylay me.'

'Do you know anything about this?' I asked Rungano. He had been a full year out here and I had just been employed here three months ago.

'About what?'

'That they all hate him?'

'I don't know. But I guess they would.'

'Why would they?'

Rungano shrugged his shoulders. 'You shouldn't have got yourself involved in this.'

'In what?'

'*Nipa* is illegal.'

'I know but I just wanted a little money.'

'No. You wanted the little adventure across the border and then bringing in that illegal stuff and selling it to them without being caught. I told you not to do it and I don't know why you went and did it.'

'That's got nothing to do with their wanting to murder him, has it?' Rungano had always wanted to be friends with me because we happened to come from the same area, not the same place, but we spoke the same dialect and there they spoke another. He always talked to me out of his one-year experience here and it could be tiring.

'I could have lent you the money, you know.'

'I know and I wouldn't have been able to pay it back in time and you would have climbed up the tallest tree to holler it to them.' It was unfair on him, but he did have that little nasty back-biting streak in him.

'You don't trust me, do you?'

I hoped he wasn't going to cry. He cried a lot when drunk.

'You know I trust you.'

'No, you don't.'

We were quiet for some time.

Then the man spoke. 'Mr Moyo, you shouldn't worry. I wouldn't tell on you. I won't mention any drinking anywhere. But I have to see the manager.'

'Don't you think we should see the Compound Foreman first?'

'Ngoro? He hates me. If you can't take me to the manager I will go alone.'

'What do you suggest?' I asked Rungano.

'I don't know,' Rungano shrugged his shoulders. 'All I know is you shouldn't have got involved in all this at all. They don't like him and now you are getting yourself involved in their family feuds.'

'Don't you think you should try and get some sleep and then see the manager tomorrow? We could get Ngoro to give us the first aid kit and –'

'You want them to finish me off, Mr Moyo? And I thought you were my only friend.'

We hadn't discussed before that we were friends although he seemed to prefer to talk to me despite my excuses of being busy. Now I wished I had paid a little more attention to him.

'I still think you should have taken him to Ngoro in the first place,' I told Rungano.

'He wanted to see you. He said you would know what to do.'

'Ngoro is in charge of the compound.'

'He said you are his only friend here.'

'Not in cases like this.'

'Mr Moyo,' the man was looking up, his left eye wide open, the right totally closed over and very shiny through the blood caking. 'Don't you trust me?' His voice carried something like the sad wind through a harvested field just before the June frosts.

'I trust you.' I didn't have any feeling of trust or hate – there was just a big feeling of resistance, of not wanting to be involved in something I didn't know. And now he was going to make me hate him for imposing such an enormous responsiblity on me.

'I don't want to see anybody, don't you see?' he said. 'They are all against me and if I don't see the manager to put a stop to this at once,

144

one day they will succeed in killing me.'

'All right,' I said.

I looked over at Rungano. He was looking at the floor, smoking his cigarette in a way that made it clear to me he didn't want to be part of this.

'What do we do?' I asked him.

He sighed. 'See Ngoro, I suppose.'

'Please, Mr Moyo –'

'He is drunk now and he wouldn't know what to say to the manager. Anyway, you are in trouble. Ngoro might decide the man isn't his responsibility too. One way or another the *nipa* would come out.'

'I am not that drunk,' the man said.

'All right. You wait here. I will be right back.' I opened the door.

'I don't want to see Ngoro or any of those men,' the man said behind me but it was too late.

Old Mangara and Chokuya were about to knock at the door when I opened it.

'We are coming to see you,' Old Mangara said.

'Oh?' I was standing in the doorway.

'Well – don't you say come in?'

Old Mangara was short, dangerously quiet when sober but very jovial and full of song and sound good logic when drunk. They said he was the local headman's chief adviser. I could tell he liked me although he was too shy to show it. Also he seemed to be a little afraid of me, afraid in an awe-struck way that I couldn't easily place. He just might help. I let them enter.

'You wouldn't have a little left over?' Old Mangara asked.

'A little what?'

'A little of the worm-killer?'

'It's finished.'

'O, come on,' said Chokuya.

'Mr Moyo –' the man was trying to stand up. He held onto the chair, both fell. He tried again and stood unsteadily to his feet.

'Mr Moyo –' the man was swaying.

145

'You have been giving him drink?' Old Mangara asked in a half-whisper.

'No.' I shook my head.

'It seems he has been in a fight,' Chokuya said studying the man closely in the dim light.

'Get away from me,' the man said weakly to Chokuya. He tried to walk to the door. Old Mangara held him back.

'What do you want from me? Get away from me.' His struggle was very feeble. Old Mangara gently pushed him onto the floor. He turned to me. 'What happened?'

'He says someone tried to kill him on his way home.'

'To kill him?'

'Yes.'

Chokuya gave an unpleasant snort.

'Who?' Old Mangara's voice sounded both excitedly conspiratorial and frightened.

'He says it's Samba.'

'Samba?'

'I want to see the manager at once,' the man said. His head lay on his drawn-up knees and his hands were locked round the knees.

Chokuya gave another snort.

Old Mangara gave him a brief terrible look and Chokuya looked away, scratching the dirty, scattered stubble on his chin.

Old Mangara squatted down in front of the man.

'Mangazva.'

The man didn't answer.

'Do you hear me? Mangazva?'

'Go away.'

'Wake up Mangazva. Do you hear me, Mangazva?'

'What do you want?'

'What happened?'

'Samba tried to kill me.'

'Where?'

'At the second curve down the road home.'

'Was he alone?'

'I am – not – quite – yes he seemed to be alone – but there could have been others as well.'

'Were *you* alone?'

'No. I was with Nyemba.'

'And where is Nyemba now.'

'He ran away.'

'Did he run away before or after Samba attacked you?'

'I don't know but when I came to he wasn't there.'

'When you came to? What do you mean when you came to?'

'He threw me down that ravine after he hit me.'

'Samba did that?'

'Yes.'

'Are you sure it was Samba?'

'Yes.'

'When did he attack you?'

'When he left this place.'

'When did you leave?'

'A little after sunset.'

'And you are quite positive it was Samba?'

There was a long silence. Old Mangara stood up but didn't look at any of us. Slowly, he said, 'It could be Samba or any of Samba's people.'

'Or he could be lying,' Chokuya said – clearly disliking Mangazva.

'Or he could be lying,' Old Mangara said in a very low slow voice.

'He is always lying,' Chokuya said and spat on top of the stove. His spittle sizzled into nothing.

'But right now he is hurt,' Old Mangara said.

'I want to see the manager,' Mangazva said.

'Look. Can you walk?' Old Mangazva was squatting before the man again.

'A little.'

'Forget about the manager –'

'I want to see the manager.'

147

'You will come with me. Let me wash those wounds and anoint them with some medicine I have got and tomorrow you will be all right.'

'I want to see the manager right now.'

'The manager is not your father,' Chokuya said.

'I am not talking to you,' Mangazva said.

'The manager is not your wife,' Chokuya said. 'You are always seeing the manager. Is he your brother?'

'The man is hurt, Chokuya,' Old Mangara said gently.

'He is only drunk and he fell – into that ravine.'

'Samba tried to kill me.'

'No one tried to kill you. You just want to make trouble for everyone here. We know you.'

'Chokuya,' Old Mangara said gently.

'The man is a damn liar and sell-out.'

'I am not talking to you Chokuya,' Mangazva said, his voice raised a little.

'I wish you were and then I'd teach you how not to talk to me forever.'

'Leave him alone, Chokuya,' Old Mangara said.

'We have left him alone for damn too long. Who does he think he is?'

'I know what you mean but right now he is hurt and he is our neighbour,' Old Mangara said.

'He is not my neighbour. And Samba didn't attack him at all. He just wants to make trouble for everyone.'

Suddenly the man was up and limping towards the door.

'Where do you think you are going?' Old Mangara tried to hold him back.

'Going to see his father, the manager,' Chokuya said. 'Let him go.'

'No, Mangazva. Let's talk things over.'

'Let me go!'

The man pushed Old Mangara back with sudden violence. He went out banging the door behind him.

'Son of – ' Old Mangara said.

'Why do you bother with him at all?' Chokuya said.

'He is going to raise trouble for everybody here.'

'Well – he isn't going to raise any trouble for *me*,' Chokuya threatened.

'You talk as if you don't know his mother.'

'And what do I care for her? She isn't the only one who knows medicines.'

'I wish you wouldn't talk like that so openly in front of her son, that's all.'

'What's wrong with his mother?' I asked.

Chokuya looked at me with clear contempt, and said, 'And you didn't have any business to be involved with him.'

'He came to me. I didn't invite him in.'

'You should have thrown him out,' Chokuya said. 'You didn't have any business to be involved with him at all.'

'But what's wrong with him?' I asked.

'His mother is the worst witch –'

'Chokuya!' Old Mangara warned.

'Everybody knows it – what's wrong with you?'

'But not everybody talks about it,' Old Mangara advised. He turned to me, 'Chokuya is right. You are new here. That man is a snake. He is worse than his mother.'

'What's he done?'

'Once there was a big fire up at North Patrol Station and some of the people are not yet out of jail,' Chokuya said. 'My two brothers are still in jail.'

'It wasn't proved that *he* sold them out,' Old Mangara said.

'But who doesn't know it? *He* burned that plantation down and *he* told the whites it was someone else.'

'There is no proof –'

'To hell with proof!' Chokuya shouted. 'What do I need proof for when my brothers are dying in that foul place?'

There was a silence.

149

'Don't let his mother hear you because tomorrow we will be burying you.'

Chokuya seemed to want to say something, then he kept quiet.

'Don't let her hear you,' Old Mangara warned.

'Tomorrow before sunup we will be singing *mbavarira* for you.'

'All right, all right,' Chokuya suddenly seemed less brave.

'I have warned you several times about that mouth of yours when you have had a little.'

'I hear you – can't you understand that?' Chokuya was trembling.

There was a silence. Chokuya went out. He didn't seem very brave any more.

Old Mangara shook his head sadly. 'Just a little beer and he thinks he knows everything.'

A little later he said, 'Moyo –'

'Yes?'

'Keep clear of that man. You understand me? Keep clear of that man. You shouldn't have sold him *nipa*.'

'I didn't know he is that type.'

'No. You wouldn't have known that. You are still new here. Anyway, keep clear of him. He is bad poison. He and his mother. His father, poor bastard, is really all right. But him and his mother, keep clear of them.'

Old Mangara went out, less drunk than when he had come in.

Rungano coughed. 'Well, I warned you, didn't I?' he said.

I didn't answer him. I felt very, very tired.

'I warned you.'

'Yes, you did.'

'But you wouldn't believe me.'

'No.'

'You still don't believe me, do you?'

'No.'

'Please, Ngoni!'

'Just leave me alone, will you?' I had a terrible headache.

'You think you know everything, don't you?'

We glared at each other.

'I want to go to bed,' I said. I closed the pot of sadza and pushed it close to the stove. I didn't feel hungry any more.

'Good night Ngoni,' Rungano said and went out. He closed the door very softly behind him.

Rungano was very careful never to pick a quarrel with anyone. The closest he ever came to a quarrel was always with me.

I sat down in the chair and looked at the stove.

I wondered why this unreasonable fear always came upon one when you thought you were long past that kind of thing. I tried to steady my thoughts on the stove and not think about my fear. It was useless. I looked at my hands. They were shaking slightly. I knew I would have the nightmares again that night. Fighting snakes all night long and waking up soaked in sweat. I knew I would light the candle and smoke cigarette after cigarette remembering every witch story I had heard since early childhood right up to the present quarrels with my parents.

Now my parents were over three hundred miles away, a distance I had deliberately calculated to put between us, and now it seemed as if they were sitting in the same room with me.

'Wherever you go don't you ever think you will never come back. Your parents are your parents, don't you forget it.'

I had come up here to be alone, to forget certain unnamed pains one always seemed to be inflicting on others, despite one's wish not to.

There was the constant squeak and groan of boughs rubbing against each other down in the ravine. The candle guttered in the wind. I stood up and closed the window. Chikara Forest Research Station was on the slope of a mountain. At the foot of the mountain ran Chikara River and our compound was built right above the river. I always felt that were there to be a landslide we would all be hurled two hundred feet down into the river. But I liked to walk under the old trees in the ravine where you had to follow already cleared paths because of the thick vegetation and creepers. Even in the driest months it was always wet under those wet mossy trees which completely shut out the sky above.

151

Out of the ravine, on top of Chikara, there was the endless view of the blue mountains down into Mozambique. I didn't need anyone to keep me company with all this.

But now it seemed that one must always have company.

'Come in!'

The door opened and Mangazva came in.

He had a clean bandage round his head and diagonally across the face, covering the right eye and ear. The top of the head was bare. The minor cuts and bruises had been cleaned and treated with some dark ointment.

'You are back,' I didn't know what else to say to him. After what I had just been told about him, he suddenly seemed very dangerous in a dark midnight kind of way.

'Yes I am back.'

He was standing by the door, awkward, undecided on what to do next, as if he had forgotten a message he had been asked to deliver. He looked sadly harmless.

'What did Mr Jones say?'

'The manager?'

'Yes.'

'He told me to bring Samba up to see him tomorrow morning.'

He shifted from his left foot to the other. 'You needn't worry about – about – that – Mr Moyo.'

'Take a seat,' I pushed a chair towards him.

'No. I must really be going home.' He was quiet for some time. 'I would like to – to – thank you, Mr Moyo.'

'For what?'

'You heard them? They all hate me here.'

I didn't say anything.

'It's dark now,' he said, searching for something inside him.

'Yes, it's dark.'

'Mr Moyo –'

'Yes?'

'I want to thank you. You needn't worry about that – that – *nipa*. I

152

didn't say anything about you or anyone although no one would believe me here if I said so.'

'Forget it. People are like that.'

'I would like to forget it very much but they won't let me.'

I didn't say anything.

'Mr Moyo –'

'Yes?'

'You believe me when I say I didn't say anything to the manager?'

'Yes. I believe you.'

'Thank you.' He seemed to get lost inside himself again. Then he said, 'You know what the manager did to me, Mr Moyo?'

'No. What did he do?'

'He laughed at me.'

'Oh.' It seemed to bother him that the manager had laughed at him.

'The manager said that he didn't care that I had been drinking but I would be in trouble if the case were taken to the police.'

'Did you tell him you had been drinking?'

'He knew that without my telling him. Then he asked me if I wanted the case forwarded to the headman.'

'And?'

'I said yes and he laughed and asked me whether the headman was my uncle. I said he isn't and he and his wife laughed and he told me to forget it like a man.'

'And so you should.'

'He laughed at me, Mr Moyo.'

'Forget it.'

'You know I have chopped wood for him and dug his garden for him – for nothing, Mr Moyo – for nothing, and he laughs at me when I was nearly murdered.'

His voice sounded very bad. I noticed he was shivering.

'Come closer to the fire.' I raked the coals in the stove and got the fire going.

'No, don't let me bother you.'

'It's no bother at all.'

153

'I'll go home, Mr Moyo. Mother will be worried.'

He seemed worried about his mother. I didn't say anything then. Mention of his mother brought back Old Mangara's warning. I found myself resisting him again, wishing him gone, yet at the same time feeling guilty that I should want to turn him out on such a night and hurt him like this.

'But you can't walk like this. It's at least four miles down to your home.'

'I think I can make it. I must see mother. She will be worried and I know she won't sleep. My wife is all right.'

'You *are* married?' Somehow I hadn't thought of him being married at all. Now that he mentioned it he seemed to change in my relationship with him.

'I have got three children. Aren't you married, Mr Moyo?'

'No.'

'You *are* lucky.'

'Why?'

He hesitated. Was he about to let me into another family secret?

'Well – it's just a way one feels, I suppose. Anyway, it was mother who pushed me into it, I was all for giving myself a few more years.'

I didn't feel safe talking about his mother so I said lamely, 'Look – you can put up here tonight and go home tomorrow.'

He thought it over and shook his head. 'You see. I have never slept out and I can't start that today. Mother will –'

'All right, I'll take you down.'

'You –' he seemed to brighten up, then his face fell again. 'No. I'll manage. It's just that it's so dark – and – no, Mr Moyo I wouldn't trouble you at all. They would begin to talk and I couldn't have that happen to you. After all you have done for me.'

What had I done for him? I knew I had to take him home. He wanted me to take him home but he couldn't bring himself to say it openly. He was being tricky in the only way people like him could be. Making himself unworthy of my friendship, putting me at a disadvantage. He was using me and I suddenly felt hemmed in, constricted.

He was smiling foolishly and shivering.

'Here.' I handed him my jacket.

He clapped his hands boyishly and took the jacket. It didn't have any buttons and he had to hold it together in front to keep himself warm.

'You wouldn't have a cigarette?'

I gave him a cigarette. I knew he always smoked the coarse labourers' hand-rolled ones.

He had some difficulty in lighting the cigarette. With one eye covered, he had lost his sense of distance. He held the cigarette an inch or two away from the candle flame, drew on it, realised it wasn't lit, and tried again. He made five unsuccessful attempts to light that cigarette and I had to finally light it for him.

'Thank you,' he said.

I didn't say anything as I led him out of the room. I didn't lock the kitchen because I shared it with Rungano who was right now in his own room and might want to make a cup of coffee or sit at the fire before turning in.

Mangazva waited for me outside my room as I went in to put on my coat.

I locked the door and we started down the mountain road to his home. I was worried that we would run into some of the men at the station. We didn't.

Like most of the general labourers who worked in these forestry plantations, Mangazva lived with his parents at their home and he came up to work every morning. The compound was for those whose homes were too far from the station and special employees who worked in the offices as clerks or in the seed laboratory as research assistants.

The descent down the mountain was quite steep and there were over twenty curves to ease the sharp gradient in the four miles between the station and the floor of the valley where Mangazva's home was.

The pine tree plantation was moving down from the mountain sides into the valley and several new compounds were being built to accommodate those who lost their homes to the Forestry Commission but still wanted to stay on as full-time labourers on the plantations.

'When are you going to move out?' I asked Mangazva when we came into the open of the valley floor and the homely smell of burning fires and cooking meals.

'Depends on when the plantation gets to us.'

'It shouldn't be long now. I hear some people are moving out right now.'

'After the troubles of the fire father was all for moving out but mother wouldn't hear of it.'

'Troubles of the fire?'

'So you haven't heard?'

'No.'

'Well there was a big fire in one of the plantations here and the Forestry Commission people sent a lot of our people to jail. That was when I used to help Mr Jones with chopping wood, digging up in his garden and going into town with him in the truck. We were great friends then.'

He seemed eager to talk of his friendship with Mr Jones so I asked, 'Aren't you still great friends now?'

'Mr Moyo, people are jealous.'

'What happened?'

'They started circulating rumours that I had been responsible for getting all those people arrested because what did I hang around Mr Jones for when I didn't eat with him? It was very bad for us, that time. Father wanted to move out but mother wouldn't hear of it. There were bitter quarrels but mother is very tough and father sort of lost his toothhold and slid off into a kind of sleepwalking living and a terrible illness of the mind.'

There was a sudden rush of foul-smelling air from the swamp close to the village.

'Mother is still great friends with Mr Jones but it's wearing thin now, like the hairs on the hide of a much-used mangy dog. You see, mother had an idea that one day Mr Jones would adopt me and send me to school – to university even, so that I wouldn't have to do any of this back-breaking work I am doing now. She used to bring him baskets and baskets of tomatoes, potatoes, vegetables from our garden – free of charge, you understand? Even peanut butter, but Mr Jones didn't send me to any school. And mother still feels very bad about it that he didn't send me to school. You see, I am the only son and I grew up with a weak chest and mother thought I would die.'

Mangazva suggested that we take a longer way that wouldn't involve us in passing through other people's homes.

'Even now I don't understand why Mr Jones did that to us. And today he laughed at me. After all we have done for him.'

He was quiet for some time then said, 'Mother thinks Mr Jones won't move us out to some drier place when the plantation gets to us but after today, I am not sure any more. Father might have been right after all.'

On a little rise in the middle of the valley was Mangazva's home.

'We were a little farther down the valley and we built here soon after I started helping Mr Jones up at the station. Mother used to take me a little higher up the hill – there is a nice view of the whole valley from up there – and she would stride about pegging out the length and width of the house she thought I would build after I finished school.'

He gave a short laugh.

'You know the Bonzai family? That big white house you see glittering on the side of the mountain the other side of the valley?'

'Yes. But I don't know the people who own it.'

'Those are my mother's people. My uncle – a headmaster at St Michael's – built it for his parents. My other two uncles are both heads of some very big schools somewhere near Harare. That's where you come from, isn't it?'

'Yes. Somewhere near there.'

'Yes. I knew that you must come from somewhere near there the first day I saw you.'

'Why would you think that?'

157

'One can always tell these things you know. But,' he coughed, 'why did you leave such a beautiful place to come out here?'

'Have you been there?'

'Your place?'

'Harare.'

'I hope to go out there some time. I will try to get one of my uncles to invite me.'

'Maybe you won't like it once you are there.'

'Oh but I am sure I shall like it. I am quite certain I shall.'

We stopped talking as we entered the yard. Mangazva greeted his dog, Muroyindishe and we entered the 'big house'.

There were two huts on the north and south sides of the big house. The big house was dark and menacing. It was too big and too high for the family it guarded: Mangazva's father and mother, Mangazva, his wife and three small children. Part of the roof was thatched with grass and the other part was of corrugated iron sheets. Little rocks and blocks of bricks were placed as weights on the roof to keep the sheets from flying away in the heavy hailstorms that sometimes built up in these mountain areas. Whenever the wind blew there was a constant irritating flap-flap from some loose sheets on the roof.

Rags and bits of plastic paper plugged spaces between the roof and the top of the wall. Walking into the house you felt very small and self-conscious from the distance your eye had to travel to reach the ceiling. Although Mangazva said they had all been living in this house for the past ten years, one had the feeling that they had just moved in – it gave me that queer feeling of being unlived in, a feeling I always associated with tobacco sheds or large abandoned factories which seem too hostile and too cold to give warmth to our frail and naked dreams.

The big house was clearly unfinished and it was already fading into the past with that painful apology that haunts people who never seem able to handle the simple affairs of everyday living.

'This is the big house,' Mangazva said as he knocked on the door. 'Mother built it in preparation for my wedding but the in-laws said

158

there couldn't be a wedding till I had paid three-quarters of the lobola for their daughter. When we finally paid the third quarter she was already living with us and expecting her third child.'

Her third child? It was the tone he had used that bothered me.

'Where have you been?' The mother was in the doorway slowly losing her anger and certainty as she realized that her son wasn't alone.

'Mother, this is Mr Moyo, the new research assistant up at the station. I have told you about him. He is my best friend.'

I tried to smile in the dark. I shouldn't have bothered. She knew me already.

'Yes but you didn't tell me he would bring you home with a bandage over half your face and the stink of *nipa* on your breath one day.'

'Mother, Mr Moyo helped –'

'. . . you to a full drum of *nipa* and carried you halfway to your grave.'

He raised his hands to explain. She turned and strode back into the dark interior of her fading dreams and rotting wedding present. Her footsteps echoed like the soft thuds of dry earth on a coffin in an oversize grave.

I followed Mangazva in the wake of his mother's wrath to a dark little tight cavern at the far end of the big house. There was a little fire in a smoke-darkened corner, no chimney and a rickety table and some chairs set close by. This was all the living space they now required, and, although smoke from the fire stung their eyes, none of them dared to venture into the crouching darkness behind their backs.

'Mangazva!' the wife gasped softly when we came into the dim light of the fire. She was sitting in one of the chairs, a little farther away from the fire. Mangazva's father didn't turn to look. He seemed to have been a long time growing into his chair, so that he had become part of it like one of those strange parasite plants that one often sees growing from the branches of some very old trees. His shoulders were hunched, his head bent forward towards the fire as if he were listening

159

to the stories the fire was telling him, stories of a much warmer, distant country.

The softer, more comfortable seat closer to the fire belonged to the mother. It was an old wornout bucket seat that was mellowing with constant usage but whose springs screamed each time they were reminded of their past existence. Mangazva's mother had eased their painful memory of bumpy roads and a premature scrap-heap grave with cushions and now they faithfully served her much-abused back-side and caressed the edges of her memory with much travelled fingers.

Mangazva pulled two chairs close to the fire.

'Come to the fire, Mr Moyo.'

I would have preferred to remain a part of the darkness behind their backs.

The mother hissed and closed her eyes.

Now, we formed an irregular semi-circle round the fire. The only people who seemed to be very still were Mangazva's father, who seemed to be feeling the chair's cankerous roots as they ate deeper into him, and Mangazva's wife who was silently reading her husband's daily misadventures in his face. She was just looking at him, not letting her face pronounce words.

Mangazva fidgeted a bit before he announced, 'This is my friend, Mr Moyo.' I felt the constriction in the cramped living quarters of this house and infinite space at my back. I moved to some impossibly safe place inside me.

No one answered, no one moved. I realized that if I let all my weight sit in that chair we would both fall. So I concentrated on that strange game where you clinically balance two tensions at their extremes to maintain a very subtle equilibrium. Perhaps Mangazva hadn't realized that he had condemned me to the worse of the two chairs. Only the ancestral spirits of chairs still held it together.

'Samba wanted to kill me on my way here,' Mangazva told them and once again I felt the long distance I had to travel to get the real feeling of that word: kill.

'Say that again?' The mother was animated. The springs of her seat screamed as she turned round to look at her son.

'Samba tried to kill me.'

Mother and wife looked at him, the former rearranging certain misplaced things in her mind and the latter trying to leave them as they were.

'You really mean that?' The clouds were very low in the sky of her mind.

'I have never lied to you before, mother, have I?'

From a secret place only suffering plants can tell you about, his father croaked, 'If only you learned to live with people properly, you wouldn't have all this happen to you.'

'Properly how? Ask Mr Moyo there. He saw it all. Wasn't it Samba who attacked me first, Mr Moyo?'

I suppose there are depths and depths, colours and colours to the fable called truth.

The chair creaked suddenly and broke. I fell on my back.

'O, I am so sorry, Mr Moyo –' Mangazva said.

'Give him the other chair,' the mother said.

'You aren't hurt, Mr Moyo?' Mangazva said, handing me the chair he had been sitting in. He went back into the darkness of the house and brought an old oil tin which he sat on.

'And I don't know how many times I keep telling the men of this house to buy some new chairs.'

'You know I am going to, mother,' Mangazva said.

'You know I am going to, mother,' the mother mimicked. She sigh-hissed again, 'Well, never heard of a dog that gave birth to a goat.'

'And do you know why they fought, Mr Moyo?' Her voice surprised me. It just didn't sound her age at all. It was too old. I turned round and she was now looking directly at me: Mangazva's wife.

'It wasn't a fight, do you hear me?' Mangazva barked with sudden violence, turning round to his wife. 'You sit on your ears when people talk? I said Samba attacked me and when I came to I was in Mr

161

Moyo's arms. It was Mr Moyo who took me up to the station to have my wounds dressed.'

'Well – if it's Samba then I think I have just about had enough of him and his family,' the mother was talking in a very low but firm voice. 'I think I have just had enough and tomorrow it's either them who leave this area or I die, I don't know how many times I have had to put up with their gossip, back-biting, and name-blackening! I am going to see Samba's father tomorrow.'

Mangazva pulled out his shirt furiously and said, 'Look!' He went and knelt by his mother's side, pulling his shirt higher up to his armpits. 'Feel here, mother! You feel the bump? And here – you feel the lump? And the bruises? Do you feel the bruises, mother? Do you feel them, mother? The marks of the stones he hit me with! Do you feel them?'

His mother was moving her hand up and down Mangazva's back, chest and sides, feeling the marks the stones had left.

There was a silence as Mangazva went to sit down. His mother had cried and now her mouth and face were set. She asked, 'You said you went to see Mr Jones?'

'Yes. His wife dressed the wounds.'

'And what did *he* say about Samba?'

'He laughed at me.'

'He whaaat?'

'Ask Mr Moyo there, he –'

'I said don't involve your Mr Moyo in this,' the father said quietly.

'But those people nearly killed your son and you sit there –'

She stopped and let it all roll silently around us. I could almost touch it, whatever it was that she had, that she could throw at you without words, just her look, and I felt I was very far away from home and the smell of familiar faces. I wanted to leave that house immediately but I couldn't.

'If you stopped this drinking and coming home late and tried to grow up and lived with people properly –' his father stopped too. His voice was gruff and hoarse but firm in a way that I hadn't expected it to

162

be. He seemed to be concentrating on something that he could feel right there where he sat.

Now he was finishing what he had started to say, '. . . and if you stopped running to your mother's skirts each time you feel a sneeze coming up, you might at last be able to help yourself and your wife and children.' And his head fell slightly forward. All the time he had been talking his wife had been looking away at the wall nearest her.

Now she turned her head and clicked her tongue against the roof of her mouth. 'Barking dogs and castrated bulls.' She spat into the fire.

The sound of it came as if from a long distance away. At first I thought it might be a puppy with diarrhoea, then I realized it was a human voice. I looked round at Mangazva's wife.

She was holding her belly with her hands, pressing it hard inside.

Her face seemed to swell out in a criss-cross maze of veins. She was sweating. Then it was all over. I had thought she had been carrying, but she wasn't.

She spoke clearly into the quietness of the room, 'Mr Moyo?'

'Yes, Ma?'

'Are you really my husband's friend?'

I didn't know what to say, so I nodded my head, just slightly, for her alone, and I hoped she would understand so that they could let me go free. What had I done?

'Do you drink too?' Her voice was loud and clear. I wondered whether I had done her wrong in my silent agreement to her husband's lying.

'No,' I told her truthfully. I had stopped drinking a year or so back.

Mangazva looked at me as if I had slapped him in the face. I thought I saw a flicker of life in the mother's face, I wasn't sure. But she sighed, crossed her hands and looked into the fire. Her face said nothing of the past storm. The fire lent it a slow glow that seemed to come out from somewhere inside her. She could be beautiful when she tried.

'Mr Moyo?' Mangazva's wife said.

'*Ma*?'

'Would you please help me?'

I felt the resistance building up, but I knew I would not know how to use it.

'How?'

'Help my husband stop his drinking.'

I looked at Mangazva. He was just staring into the fire as if he didn't hear or feel anything.

'When you see him drunk,' Mangazva's wife was saying, 'when you see him drunk up there at the station, give him a place to sleep or bring him down as you have done tonight.'

Something tightened in me but the mother rescued me. She turned her full glowing face on her daughter-in-law and said, 'Your husband is neither a beggar nor a tramp. He has a home. He has never ever slept out and he isn't going to start that today. And I don't think he needs Mr Moyo or anyone to bring him home because he rarely comes home after dark.' She turned towards the fire and resumed her former posture. 'Thank you, Mr Moyo,' she said into the fire.

Quickly, Mangazva's wife rose and disappeared into the darkness behind us. I heard the door open and close.

I stood up.

'Goodnight,' I said to no one in particular.

'Goodnight, son. And try and help him, you know.' I was surprised that Mangazva's father was still awake. I had thought him dead.

Mangazva instantly woke up. He had been sleeping with his eyes open.

'You are going, Mr Moyo?'

'Yes. Goodnight.'

'No. I will see you out.'

'Sit down, Mangazva!'

'Mother, please!'

'I said sit down.'

'I will just see him to the door.'

And he accompanied me to the door and out.

It was very dark.

164

We stopped at the edge of the yard.

'Mr Moyo.'

'Yes?'

'I don't know how to thank you.'

'O, for heaven's sake!' I turned to go but he held me by the sleeve of my coat.

'You are forgetting your jacket.'

I took it.

'And here –' he put something in my hand.

'What's this –'

'Just to oblige me. Open it up.'

I knew what it was.

'You should really try and stop drinking you know,' I told him as the strong smell of *nipa* attacked my nostrils.

'It's a long way up there Mr Moyo and the night is a bit chilly.' His voice seemed to have aged. He really sounded sincere. I smelled the stench from the swamp up the valley and sudden remorse filled me.

'Just to oblige me,' he said. 'Here, I will take the first sip to take out the witchcraft, as we say.'

He drank and handed me the bottle. By the weight of the bottle, he hadn't drunk much.

'I know you drink but you have only stopped for some time to do what you want to do. Well, break the fast just for one day, for my sake.'

He sounded quite sincere.

It was *nipa*, and much stronger than that I had sold him early that evening up at the station.

'Good?' he was eager to know.

'Very good.'

'I am glad you like it.'

Suddenly, an old carelessness invaded me. I felt a lightheadness I hadn't felt in a long, long while. The books I was studying for my 'A' levels could take a day's holiday.

I tilted my head back and gulped the throat-scratching chest-burning stuff in one long breath.

I handed him the bottle.

I wiped my mouth and turned away, leaving him holding the bottle.

'Mangazva!'

'O, damn damn her!'

He gasped, 'Mr Moyo. But you *are* a drinker!'

Then I heard little stones rolling as he scrambled back to his mother.

She was waiting for me a little farther down the path to the station.

My head buzzed when she called my name. I had that momentary disorientation that explodes into panic without warning.

'It's me, Mangazva's wife.'

I released breath slowly. I didn't say a thing.

'I just wanted to remind you that I really meant what I said. Anyway, you lied to me. You drink and you said you didn't. Forget the request. I also wanted to warn you that my husband suffers from mental disturbances. Right now he is sleeping in a room very close to his parents' in the big house. I sleep with the children in one of the little huts.'

She was talking very fast, breathing very heavily.

'I wanted him so much to have a very close friend. I don't care about the drinking. It is what his mother is doing to him. I could have left him years ago but I really love him, you know. And he can really be lovable, sometimes.'

She was quiet again. Then her voice changed. 'No. I don't think you can be friends with him. His mother would be too strong for you. She would – you know – crush you just like – like –'

She was quiet again. The breathing heavier.

'You will help me, won't you?' Her voice broke, lost.

Then she withdrew backwards into some bushes and I heard her hurriedly going up to the house.

I saw the night light that was always on every night at the station but there was the immediate darkness – four thick miles of it. The *nipa* might help but it is not advisable to take *nipa* on an empty stomach

166

and I hadn't eaten a thing since breakfast. Well, there was the station light – and bed.

I took the first step as if I were walking into a bog. The stench from the swamp was stronger than before. Always when you thought you were quietly walking along, safe and alone, there was the sudden screech of tyres and the smell of burnt rubber to remind you that you were in the middle of a very busy thoroughfare. When you thought you were walking on firm ground suddenly the earth gave way and you were being sucked down into quicksand faster than you could breathe till you were just part of the bubbles that disturbed the surface of the swamp. And so I stumbled on, sometimes breaking into a run, sometimes walking, stumbling, falling, groping, rising in an insane rhythm only darkness knows and in my throat was a lie as thick and frightening as the night: *No, I will not help you!*

——16——

The Day the
Bread Van Didn't Come

Mrs Pfende's eyes shifted from the whimpering dog on the chain making circles round and round the solitary tree in the dusty yard, to the single dry bun in the wire-cage. She listened once more: no sound.

'I wonder why it is so late today.' Her husband spoke from a corner of the shop where he was making irritating snifflings and reading a week-old paper. She paid as much attention to him as to the close, stifling little shop that reeked with the stink of dry salted fish, dust and cheap soap.

'Or he is ill,' she said almost to herself and immediately bit her lip, afraid of her own thought. Her eyes once more looked past the door into the wind-swept yard. The short grass beyond the yard had gone yellow and brittle. It was August, the time of grass fires. The wind raised dust, mealie husks and leaves into the air. The dog in the yard stopped its moaning. It stood looking into the shop with watery eyes as if it had begun to lose hope of anyone ever coming to free it.

'Why don't you release that dog and let it go wherever it wants to go?' She spoke without looking at her husband. He didn't quite hear her. He raised his big head and said: 'You said?'

'The dog,' she almost barked and he winced. 'Why don't you let it go?' She was glaring at him and he withdrew into himself from her violence.

'Too much mischief. She'll be useless to me once she gets herself full of puppies.'

'At least you could sell the puppies. Would give you much more

168

than you're getting out of this tired little hovel anyway.' But she wasn't speaking to him any more, her eyes had shifted to the dry shrivelled bun in the cage, now covered in mould. Her husband looked at her, meaning her to repeat what she had said but afraid to ask her. He returned to his reading wondering what she had said, afraid to ask her, but even more afraid that it might be a question that he had been meant to answer. He prepared himself for the inevitable violent: 'You deaf?'

'I hope nothing serious has happened,' she said and he sighed, knowing that what she had said before had not been for him. There were many things that his wife said that were not meant for him now.

'Having no bread is serious enough,' he said uneasily.

'He might have had an accident,' she said, worried. She wasn't looking at him and she looked a bit sad – undefended – so he gathered up enough courage to say: 'Accident or no accident, we should have bread today. It's practically all that sells these days. Wish I had had that phone installed.'

'He will come,' Mrs Pfende assured herself. 'Oh he will come all right,' but her heart wouldn't stop beating. 'Yes, he just has to come.' Her husband looked at her furtively and hid himself behind his paper, glad that her violence was directed at something out there or inside her. 'Must be her time of month,' he said to himself thanking God that he could make such statements about her inside himself without her hearing him. A way of getting his own back at her, he chuckled with a little comforting satisfaction, but only to himself. He hid further into himself to enjoy the feeling. Why hadn't he thought of it earlier? Her time of month, of course.

A lonely sunspot was cast on the cement floor near the centre of the shop by a single shaft of light which pierced a hole through the roof. Mrs Pfende studied it, wondering whether it was warmer there than in the rest of the darkened shop.

A little girl came in, basket in one hand and a twenty-five cent piece in the other. She stood on tiptoe the other side of the rickety wooden counter, her tiny smooth child's hand with the money held up to the counter. Mrs Pfende brought her head forward and smiled at the girl as she took her hand with the money. The girl smiled shyly back and lowered her eyes to her hand which Mrs Pfende still held. Mrs Pfende could feel the slight tension in the girl's fingers as she resisted her.

'Whose child are you?'

'Kurima's.'

'Which Kurima – up the hill or near the school?'

'Up the hill – could I have two loaves white bread please?'

'Bread is finished. I haven't seen you before. Do you live with your parents?'

'But I have seen you several times when you used to come to the women's club at the school.'

'Oh yes. I was still new in these parts then. I don't go there anymore now.'

'Why?'

'Why? I – don't know I suppose – I'm getting a bit old.'

'My mother is much older than you but she still attends the women's club.'

'O, does she now?'

'Yes, and she said – she said –' the girl looked down at her hand – she wanted to be released but Mrs Pfende held on to it. She looked down at her big toe and began to trace circles on the floor with it.

'Come, come. What did your mother say about me. I bet it was something nice. I bet she said she and I were best friends. Didn't she say that or didn't she?'

The girl nodded eagerly thinking that now Mrs Pfende would surely let go her hand but Mrs Pfende tightened her grip. 'Come on now. Don't lie to me. Good girls don't lie and you are a bright little good girl and I bet you beat them all in class. Here,' she fumbled behind the counter with her other hand, 'have a sucker. Now, what is that nice thing your mother said about me?'

'She – they were saying tha – that there is something wrong with you. Could I have the bun as well – Mother gave me a cent,' the girl hurriedly withdrew her hand to take out the cent which she held

170

together with the twenty-five cents with her other hand.

'O, that. That's the only one left. I don't think you would like it. It's rather old and dry and so mouldy like me! ha ha ha!' Mrs Pfende's poor joke failed to register with the girl.

'I don't mind it.' The girl was persistent.

'I wouldn't give such a clever girl like you such an old, dried-up –'

'Oh come on. Give the girl the bun. There is nothing wrong with it,' her husband had risen from his corner, coming towards the cage. The sight of money momentarily making him forget his wife's time of month.

'Surely you aren't going to sell her that dried-up turd, are you?' Mrs Pfende protested, something twisting inside her for the girl all mixed up with a slow-rising hatred for her husband. But he knew that as long as he didn't let his eyes meet hers he would be all right. He picked up the bun and held it out to the girl. 'Here Tombi. Good bun. Only one cent. There. That's a good girl.' The girl looked at the bun dubiously, then at Mrs Pfende who turned her head away.

'You don't like good bun?' Mr Pfende coaxed pleadingly and Mrs Pfende moved away from them to her corner of the shop. The girl looked at her, turned back, timidly proffered the cent with the left hand and removed the right, in which, fingers tightly closed over it, was the twenty-five-cent piece, off the counter. Mr Pfende took the cent, dropped it into the almost empty moneyslot at the back of the counter and gave the girl the bun. He rubbed his hands together – the first sale of the day – and stood at the counter waiting for the next customer.

The girl turned away from the counter, not daring to look in Mrs Pfende's direction, and ran out of the shop. Outside, she stopped and examined the bun, mouldy and very dry, it made a crunching sound on eating, like steel cartwheels on gravel. She looked guiltily back towards the shop and turned away to run home. Mrs Pfende had moved where she could see her and now she was listening to that familiar sound which would not come. She sighed heavily, took up her knitting from the upended Coca-Cola case on which she now sat and

171

began to knit.

After a long while with her mind on the knitting, she said, 'He has never been this late before.' Her husband knew it wasn't addressed to him, so he ruffled his paper to a new page, and spoke without addressing anything to anyone. That way, he knew, they could go on talking, listening to the sound of their voices, for the little comfort it gave each of them in his own private way, but without really touching each other. In its slack moments, which were now increasing day by day since Matiure set up his shop next to them three months ago, the shop could grow so depressingly empty and silent that their loud monologues seemed preferable to their own thoughts. 'Wish I had had that phone put in. I would have got him sacked.'

'Matiure has been only three months in business yet he has got a phone and a radio in his shop,' Mrs Pfende said despairing of ever having a telephone in this shop, realizing suddenly what a help the telephone would have been, especially now, today. Or even a radio. But better the telephone than the radio: today, or any other day, the telephone would have been much better. She would have loved to speak on the telephone, any day, every day. She wondered whether she would have been able to recognize his voice on the phone, whether it would have given her the same excitement that it gave her when they were together, face to face. Probably she would have lost the other thing – the way his whole face moves when he is talking, letting it say those things which are only superfluous to people who really understand each other when the mouth repeats them. Now she realized how little he talked when they were together, even in those daily fifteen-minute breaks which her life with her husband allowed. She now wondered whether he would have been able to excite her on the phone as he did in person, in those day-to-day fifteen minutes he would be in the shop, signing papers for the bread, asking this and that, talking slowly about how he had been three times disappointed by girls he had been about to marry, finding only too late that they were already engaged to someone else, or like that girl he actually caught in bed with another man when she knew he was coming to her place . . .

172

Would he have been able to put all that into the little cramped mouthpiece of the telephone? Mrs Pfende thought not, but at least a telephone, for any rainy day, would have been far better than the radio. . .

'With a telephone I would have as sure as hell got him sacked by now,' her husband was saying against her thoughts.

'Just because he is late today?' Mrs Pfende said sharply, looking up at her husband. He knew she was looking at him. He hadn't meant to touch her, now he had, so he brought his head very close to the paper and read with his eyes so close to it that his thick glasses nearly caressed the page. He would wait for her to get away from him.

From a safe distance he heard her say: 'He is coming. I am sure there is an explanation for this. It's just a delay, something wrong with his truck or something just gone wrong that hasn't got anything to do with him and he is safe. Oh, he is coming all right. He has never been this late before.'

Mr Pfende held his head up stiffly as if he had received a jab in the nape of the neck. He had had his little suspicions which he had, as a man too busy with the shop should, dismissed as being too damned petty, but now he wasn't sure any more. He hadn't been reading when his wife said that. He had heard her and he knew well her voice when she was excited in that way he knew so well from their first days when, pleasantly exhausted from running the shop all day, they would put out the light after the cup of coffee and turn in. He had been getting less of that voice since a year or more ago and here it was now. He had heard her right and he couldn't hold off touching her now although he knew he would regret it later but damn it, a man had his rights over a woman he had paid lobola for, hadn't he? Even without the other thing which they all thought made a marriage a marriage, which he, regrettably and unfortunately, through no fault of his own – although they wanted to believe otherwise – hadn't been able to give her, the children, he meant to say, though it pained him hard to say it out – still, a man had his rights over a woman he had paid lobola for, hadn't he? He said it to her, although he wasn't looking at her: 'I don't care how many times he has been or hasn't been late I'd have had him thrown out on his arse today and had someone with a sense of duty and business brought in.'

He waited stiffly, with a palpitating heart, for her to come.

And she did, but as if to herself, however, which was even more painful for him, because it was as if he wasn't there, for her, dismissed and done with: 'O, sense of duty and business, from your mouth? Call yourself a man with a sense of duty and business?'

She said it so resignedly it might not have been meant for him, which was a lie, on the contrary, it couldn't have showed him better what she felt had she shouted it – with what he had discovered now and the blare of the radio which someone had suddenly turned full blast on, and just as quickly, turned low in Matiure's shop down the road.

He tried again, the rustling of his paper sounding awkwardly like a bird ruffling its feathers: 'People gone without bread just because a son of –'

She cut him softly into two: 'Better a son of a bitch than a father of nothing,' then, her voice going sinisterly softer, folded him up: 'Why don't you sell up and turn baker then, if you are that hot?' Then she laughed derisively, wonderingly: 'I just wonder what kind of bread you would make – all doughy and watery, I suppose?' She laughed again mysteriously to herself, going out of his reach, towards something he could clearly guess at but never ever reach. It was new to him, this laugh of hers, and it frightened him. It said all that he had thought she would never say, all that he had been afraid she would one day have to say to him.

He had never been able to give her children. And he hadn't known that a laugh could carry such meaning in the shadows of its folds.

He tried to pull her back to something simpler: 'You always find faults with me, don't you?'

And he hadn't known that the way a mouth moves without saying anything can carry so much shadow in its meaning. She was now knitting furiously, her profile to him, and he realized that she was

174

knitting a man's jersey, for him, he also knew, and suddenly couldn't remember ever hearing her asking him whether he would like her to knit him something.

Mr Pfende put away the paper and took up the reckoner. Had she heard? He didn't think so. But then she just might have heard. What they said about him. Behind his back of course. People like throwing dirty things at other people. People like dressing up a man they know is ten times their better in a muddy suit and parading him through the village, making him dance while they laugh round their fireplaces. Now, had any of this got to her ears? That he had sold his power to make children for medicine to be successful in business? Of course, in their eyes, she was being misused. She had every self-respecting house-wife's sympathy, and was therefore a tragic figure, someone special, unlike them. Her husband who had died had given her two boys but, being a woman, the children had been taken by her husband's people and she would never see them again because her husband's people had branded her a witch and said that it had been she who had killed their brother, son, relative or whatever each of them called the deceased. Also her beauty had been reason enough for them to believe it. You are not made that beautiful without having a crack in you. And he, Pfende, had thought she could be his wife. If he had left her alone he might not have shown himself in such a bad light. The fault was in him. She could have children, he couldn't. And now she had had enough of him. He wished Matiure hadn't come spoiling things for him. Maybe his money would have been able to hold her. But then that wouldn't have soothed the wound in him: the childless-ness.

Mrs Pfende knitted furiously. She wasn't thinking of him. Some-thing tied up in her wouldn't loosen. This gave her unbelievable nervous energy.

Wind whistled on the edge of the roof and a whiff of dust blew in through the door. The dog started its circling and moaning once more. Somewhere grass was burning: the smell was on the air. The wind dropped all of a sudden and deep silence alternated with the dog's moaning.

Both of them sat in the middle of this silence: she, knitting furiously, the only way to get away from something that was painful to think about; and he: reading the reckoner with unseeing eyes all the time listening to the changes in the wind and wishing for the fiftieth time he had had that phone installed in his shop.

Once his wife said: 'There he is!' with a start. He asked who but she was unable to tell him because she was listening to something which, because it didn't come, or was heard no more, forced a disappointed sigh from her.

Much later he found himself too lonely, unused to this sudden forced silence which had come in after the revelation. So he spoke to himself: 'Two more delays like this and I'm going to sign a contract with Astron Bakery.'

He was surprised that she spoke, surprised to find that he was glad that she spoke at all, that his ear should rejoice at the sound of her voice: 'You should have thought of that earlier.'

'Didn't think it would be necessary. After all who ever thought there would be anyone else putting up shop here?' It was pleasant to talk again, to forget what had passed and talk normally of other things. He wished she would answer but she didn't. She was knitting again as always with her face that way he had learned to live with, to call normal, and he felt it would be all right if her face stayed that way even if she didn't speak, at least he would know she was all right and he was all right and he would forget that there had been a laugh that . . .

But all of a sudden the bread van was stopping in the yard. Both of them stiffened. For a moment they were both aware of each other, then the husband saw something that made him jump up almost joyously. He rushed out from behind the counter to intercept the men who were bringing in the bread.

Mrs Pfende stood up and she too saw the men coming in. Strangers. Both of them. Mr Pfende was beaming with joy: 'An accident you say?'

176

'Yes, man, didn't you hear me?' One of the men said, apparently annoyed with Mr Pfende. He had the papers. Mrs Pfende accepted them mechanically but she was very calm when she said: 'What happened?' Her voice was soft and her eyes level with the man's, who she saw, was no older than that other one. She thought she even saw a resemblance in the two faces: both boyish faces, should be eighteen or so.

'Oh, there has been this accident you see . . . terrible. Can't think about it . . . Moses . . . It was just his day . . . his day. It was that lousy bend in the road just after Christmas Pass and this timber truck just slammed into them and then silence. Terrible. Both of them. Snuffed out like that.' The young man made the *tek* sound between his thumb and middle finger. It sounded like a distant gunshot or the *crack* sound inside of lightning. 'Never knew what hit them.'

Mr Pfende suddenly laughed. Both the young man and Mrs Pfende looked at him, uncomprehending.

'What's so funny, heh?' the young man suddenly asked, dangerous, but Mr Pfende didn't look at him when he answered, still laughing: 'To think I was thinking of having him fired! Firing a dead man, hahahaha!'

'Listen, I may not know you but I know who that young man was, see? He was almost a brother to me, y'hear? And I won't have any castrated thoughtless sonofabitch laugh at him, d'y hear? I said do you hear me?' The young man had Mr Pfende by the collar, for a moment he seemed not to know what to do with him, to hit him or . . . then he just let him fall to the floor in a heap and wiped his hands against his trousers. He looked up at Mrs Pfende and said: 'You see, Moses was the best friend I ever had.'

Mrs Pfende looked at him and the young man didn't know what else to say. His face went into subtle contortions and he ended up saying: 'Well, guess the driver is impatient,' grabbed his papers and made as if to rush out but Mrs Pfende quickly grabbed him by the sleeve and said: 'I am sorry. I know Moses. He was my friend too. A great friend too, you hear me? You see I am knitting a jersey – it's almost finished –

177

which I meant to give him. . . but . . . since . . . he is . . . I . . . don't know – you wouldn't mind if – I gave to you? I mean . . . would you mind if you . . . took it . . . for the three of us . . . for . . .' She looked at him pleadingly. They looked at each other, then he began to laugh softly and said: 'Damn it if this isn't the damnedest strangest day I have been through. I don't know what to make of it all . . . ' he suddenly stopped and said: 'Hey, you shouldn't be so lonely out here in this back country with that . . . that . . .' A furtive look at Mr Pfende who was slowly rubbing his neck at the end of the counter, looking at nothing in particular, '. . . your husband?' She nodded. 'O, I am sorry . . . sure I'll take the jersey and wear it everyday of my life . . . can I have it now?'

'It isn't finished but you can certainly have it tomorrow and then we might talk a little longer . . . you see I have got two boys who should be now . . . let me see . . . thirteen and fourteen . . . and I would like you to tell me about yourself and your job and Mutare and whether you have been to Harare . . . and . . . and . . . You understand?'

The young man stared at her dumbly and said: 'Honestly, I don't understand you. You seem to be mixed up or something. I don't like running round with other men's wives if you are thinking . . . is that your husband or isn't he?'

'He is and when he knows it all I don't think he will mind. You see these boys of mine, thirteen and fourteen . . . are not here with us and he . . . isn't their father . . . but . . . I don't think he will mind when he knows it is all for the best. You see, I was too slow with Moses and now he has gone and got himself . . . '

The young man stepped back a bit and stared at her, horrified, then he spat on the floor, spun round and fled.

Mrs Pfende looked after him for some time, not understanding that he too had gone till her husband said: 'Cheeky bastard, what?' He meant everything to continue as it had been before the revelation this morning and the misunderstandings this afternoon but his wife turned on him and slapped him soundly across the cheek so that he spun and faced the wall in the back of the shop.

178

'O damn you! Damn all of you damn damn damn all of you to neverending damnation!' The door in the back of the shop slammed and she went into their bedroom where he found, five minutes later, that she had broken the glass and the frame that had carried their wedding photograph, torn up the photograph and the wedding certificate both of which she was now trying to jigsaw-puzzle together and he had to jump back and out again to attend to two customers who had come in when she said: 'Get outandtoneverendingdamnation with you!'

But he was smiling with satisfaction and his eyes glittered when he said, 'Sure, sure. We've got loads of bread.' The customers were pouring in.

And the sound of the coins, clink-clinking into the till soothed him. For the time being, things are all right, he felt. For the time being, we are holding on. He rubbed his hands which were once soap-smooth, but now, he realized with uneasiness, were subtly but surely getting chaffed and scarred.

—17—

The Flood

'We have been wondering what could have happened to you – thinking you weren't going to come,' Chitauro said.

Mhondiwa, who had announced his arrival by clapping his hands outside the hut, didn't answer. He stood just outside the door. He spoke without turning his head.

'You have done the right thing, son,' Old Makiwa said.

'Come in, come in,' Chitauro said. 'You would have disappointed me if you hadn't come. I was beginning to get worried.'

Chitauro sat opposite Old Makiwa, facing the fire and the door.

'Only the two of you?' Mhondiwa asked, still outside the door.

'Yes. This is a special party,' Chitauro said, smiling at Mhondiwa. Mhondiwa's nostrils flared, smelling danger.

'Well, don't stand there in the rain, you have delayed us long enough as it is,' Chitauro said and added with a conspiratorial smile, 'and you know how this old goat doesn't like waiting for the late-comers.'

Old Makiwa ignored this and said thickly: 'Come in, come in my son.' From the voice Mhondiwa knew that the old man was already drunk. He didn't like it that Chitauro wasn't drunk too. He went into the hut.

'What rain,' Chitauro said, rising from his seat and offering it to Mhondiwa. Mhondiwa looked at the old man and said: 'Isn't there another stool?'

'It doesn't matter,' Chitauro said. 'You aren't going to marry my

180

daughter that you should be afraid to sit where I sit.'

Mhondiwa stood awkwardly, water dripping from his clothes. He looked from Chitauro to Old Makiwa.

'Why don't you give him another stool and let us begin? The night is going,' Old Makiwa said impatiently.

'All right, all right,' Chitauro said resignedly. By the reach of his long ropy arm he pulled out another stool from a heap of blankets in a corner of the room and handed it to Mhondiwa. Mhondiwa sighed, relieved, and sat down.

'I have never seen such rain,' Chitauro said. Mhondiwa's behaviour had offended him a little and he was trying to hide his feelings. 'Can you remember a day it has rained like this, Grandfather?' Old Makiwa wasn't Chitauro's grandfather but that was to show respect.

'In the old days, yes, but then it had a special meaning,' Old Makiwa said.

'And in the dry season too?'

'Yes. July is too late and too early for such rain. This is rain for December and January. As I said, in the old days there would be a reason for it to rain like this.'

'This should be the time of winds. The sand-raising duststorms that clean the thrashing floors of chaff.'

'This rain – know what I think?'

'What do you think, Grandfather?'

'I think it is a bad sign. In the old days it rained like this before a paramount chief died.'

Mhondiwa, who had been listening to this conversation silently, wringing the water out of his coat sleeves into the fire, suddenly looked up at Old Makiwa and looked again into the fire. Chitauro noticed it and laughed uneasily. He said: 'More of your superstitions, Grandfather.'

'Superstitions? This is true – at least it was, then, when the Earth was still sacred. We always knew beforehand when anything of importance was going to happen. There were messengers.'

'That's past now,' Chitauro said firmly as if the old man was trying

181

to put wrong ideas into children's heads. 'The church has put a stop to all that.'

Mhondiwa raised his eyes a little, but he didn't let them meet Chitauro's. He was very, very quiet.

'The church?' Old Makiwa asked querulously. 'What is the church? What does the church know? It has taught my wife and children bad manners and now they tell me I am not head of the family any more because I have taken a second wife. The church – what does it know about the things that are the fruits from the seeds of the blood of this land? This rain meant something in your land, Mhondiwa?'

'I don't know. It makes me shiver.'

'I *know*. And it makes me shiver too. No, the church can say what it likes but it doesn't rain like this for nothing.'

Chitauro laughed too loudly as if to dispel the dark spell the old man was slowly casting into the room: 'It rains like this for early and better crops, doesn't it, Mhondiwa? Early maize, early millet, better rapoko, fat nuts – better and fat everything this year. Year of plenty. No famine.'

'To me – it's early death,' Old Makiwa said.

'Now, now, Grandfather,' Chitauro mock-scolded, 'none of this morbid talk is welcome here where we are all friends drinking to the year of plenty. Next year we shall all be sitting here drinking again as we are doing today.' He looked imploringly at his guests.

Old Makiwa sat with his eyes closed, his left hand touching his left side as if he felt a pain there. Mhondiwa sat motionless, not saying a thing, staring into the fire with dark fear-haunted eyes. It was that look of fear that made Chitauro feel guilty and uneasy, the look that made him desperately desire Mhondiwa's understanding and forgiveness. But Mhondiwa remembered many things and would not understand. He remembered the past and he was very afraid of Chitauro. He didn't understand Chitauro's motives for inviting him to this beer party. He only knew that once people became enemies they stayed enemies till one of them killed the other. This idea that one brewed beer to ask for forgiveness from one's enemy was new to Mhondiwa although Old Makiwa – whom he respected above everyone else – and everyone in the village compound seemed to think it the right thing to do. It wasn't that easy for Mhondiwa, who had grown up in another land and remembered too many things.

* * *

The manager, Mr Gardner, stopped the Land Rover at the edge of the plantation and came striding menacingly through the trees to where the men were working. He spoke directly to the men without bothering to go through the boss-boy, Mhondiwa.

'Everybody here!' His voice told Mhondiwa, who had started forward to intercept the manager, that things were very wrong. Mhondiwa slunk into the plantation. His heart told him that something was wrong but his mind said that the wrong was somewhere else not with him, so he went through the trees, leaping over newly-cut gumtree branches scattered all over the floor of the plantation, banging his matchet against the handaxe: 'Everybody here!' Some fear made his voice sound not quite normal. 'Everybody here!' But a strange undefined fear constricted his throat.

Through the trees, all over the plantation, the labourers in gum-stuck dirty blue overalls scurried in groups of threes and fours, wiping sweat off their brows with battered hats, headcloths and the frayed ends of their shirt sleeves.

They all gathered round the Land Rover, pruning saws, matchets and handaxes in their hands. There was a stillness in the trees which contrasted sharply with the recent memory of sawing, slashing and cutting and singing. The scent of tree gum brought tears to Mhondiwa's eyes who stood hidden among the men, not daring to go forward to stand beside the manager – as he would have normally done. The scent got mixed up in his mind with other things and he recognized the smell of death. And the manager's overcast-sky face confirmed it once and for all: something was definitely wrong and the wrong was with him, Mhondiwa. His eyes searched the ground, something pressing them down from the other people's. Intense fear and shame.

The manager spoke: 'I have decided that we are going to have a new boss-boy.' A further stillness, if this were possible, settled over the plantation and the people. Mhondiwa's eyes stung. His hand instinctively jumped to the buttons of his overalls – the boss-boy wore khaki to distinguish him from the labourers' blue – and he could feel the eyes of the men around him although he knew that they weren't looking at him directly with their eyes. They were looking at him with their *minds* and that was worse than their eyes because each of them saw different things in Mhondiwa, things that he would never know and none of them would ever reveal to him.

None of them coughed, although Mhondiwa prayed with all his heart that one of them would. They were cruelly determined to let him bear his pain alone.

'Chitauro,' the manager called. Meekly, hat crushed under left armpit, having left his tools with another man – as if going up to the manager with them in his hand would make the manager change his mind – Chitauro shuffled forward. He stood at attention before the manager.

'You are the new boss-boy,' Mr Gardner said. 'From now on you are in charge of the men. They must work or I am going to know the reason why. Right?'

'*Hongu, Nkosi.*'

'There isn't going to be any of this I was late because my goat fell into a pit yesterday and I was fixing it up or I didn't come to work yesterday because my head was aching or my wife's sister-in-law's grandmother's eldest daughter was having labour pains, right?'

'*Hinde, Mambo.*'

'And no one, no one at all – and this goes for you too Mhondiwa – no one at all is supposed to drink at work, or give the morning-after's drink pains as an excuse not to come to work. There has been too much horsing and assing around lately and I just am not going to have that any more. You want money, then you gotta sweat for it or you won't get paid for six months. Understood?'

184

'*Hinde changamire.*'

'And no one must leave his job to go to the bush or anywhere at all without telling the boss-boy. So let me not hear any more nonsense from any of you because once I do that then you know what's going to happen and where you are going. Now, back to work. Mhondiwa, come here.'

The labourers fanned out among the trees and resumed their slashing and sawing but none of them would talk immediately. There was a fearful but saddening determination in each of them to excel the other in the swing of their matchets and axes.

'Now, you,' the manager said to Mhondiwa, 'remove those overalls and get the blue from Chitauro. Good. Now if I hear again any report of insubordination or anything about you, you are going back to your grandfather's *khaya* on the double, okay?'

Mhondiwa nodded. He changed into Chitauro's blue overalls, took up his tools and went to join the other men. Chitauro remained with the manager, getting his special orders as the new boss-boy.

Mhondiwa worked in a corner of the plantation alone, at the edge of the other men. They were now talking in low tones. They stood up a little from their work when they heard the manager's car drive off. They saw Chitauro waving goodbye to the manager but Mr Gardner didn't wave back. The Land Rover disappeared up the hill to the office. Chitauro walked at a leisurely boss-boy's pace towards the men who immediately shut up and bent down to their work. Mhondiwa, all this time, was working away furiously, not paying attention to anything or anyone except the work in hand and he didn't realize that his hands had grown blisters till they gashed open and he had to wrap them up with bits of improvised bandages and went back to work, the pain in the hands easier to bear than the one inside him.

For a long time Chitauro didn't come to inspect the corner where Mhondiwa was working and Mhondiwa worked on without raising his head but when Chitauro finally came, he felt it but again he didn't stop what he was doing.

'You have done more than the others,' Chitauro said. 'I think you

185

should rest a bit.' Mhondiwa didn't hear him. He slashed at a branch, the swing of his matchet just clearing Chitauro's head by a finger's breath. Chitauro ducked. He said: 'I don't understand it. I didn't ask for it. I know he is going to do the same to me one day.'

Mhondiwa threw a bit of wood over his shoulder and again Chitauro had to raise his hands to ward off the blow. The wood grazed his arm and drew a little blood.

'Have a cigarette?' Chitauro said. Mhondiwa heard him strike a match but went on working as if he hadn't heard. He knew, with a little satisfaction, that Chitauro was having difficulty in leaving him, leaving naturally with a boss-boy's honour and swagger.

'Hey!' Chitauro said. 'It's lunch break already!' And he quickly moved away through the trees, self-consciously and too loudly banging his matchet against the axe to announce the lunch break.

Mhondiwa straightened his back. As boss-boy, he had had the advantage of going back home in the compound just close by to have his lunch instead of having it cold from a lunch pack as the labourers did. Now he walked to a secluded spot, sat on a rock and looked at his abused and bruised hands.

The other men kept away from him but he knew he had some friends among them and they just didn't want to intrude on his fresh pain with useless condolences. He knew he had friends because he had never been hard with anyone. In fact nearly everyone of the men in his gang had once received a favour of some sort from him. That was why he couldn't understand the manager's action. And he knew that Chitauro had decided to be his enemy. . .

★   ★   ★

Chitauro sighed and stood up. From an earthern platform behind him he lifted a big earthern pot frothing over with beer and placed it before Mhondiwa, then he addressed Old Makiwa: 'Grandfather, give this to my friend, Mhondiwa. Tell him that I, Chitauro, ask him to forget the past. Tell him that our elders used to say that the best test of friendship was the trial of strength, a quarrel and a fight. We have had our test of strength and now we will further strengthen the friendship with this pot of beer.'

The old man clapped his hands and said: 'You have ears, Mhondiwa, hear for yourself. Chitauro says they will remain the best of friends those who begin with a fight. And with this pot of beer he would like you to know it and forget the past like a man.' He then clapped his hands.

Mhondiwa clapped his hands and said: 'Tell him that Mhondiwa has heard everything and asks his thanks to be accepted. Tell him that Mhondiwa's belly is just a laugh of the big hungry earth, which hears and judges everything, from which everything comes and into which everything returns. And so, you, Grandfather and Chitauro, shall help Mhondiwa drink this honour and Chitauro shall have the honour to cut the beer.' He clapped in conclusion.

'No,' Chitauro shook his head. 'You hold the cup and cut the beer the way you want.'

Old Makiwa raised his hand and said: 'No, Chitauro. Guests of honour do not cut the beer for themselves. Don't you know the saying that the hand is heavier when raised to one's own mouth in the presence of friends? Since we are only three here, and you are the host and he is the guest, we shall forget that I am your elder and hold the cup for you.'

Both Mhondiwa and Chitauro clapped their hands and the old man cut the first cup for himself. He raised it to his lips and drank at length.

'Aha,' he said, wiping his mouth with the back of his hand and handing the cup to Mhondiwa, 'this is better than a woman.' And Chitauro laughed, glad of the experienced elder's compliment. He said with mock modesty: 'You exaggerate, Grandfather. Nothing can better a woman.'

'Now who is lying? I have two wives but there is only one beer for me. The best.' All three laughed and Mhondiwa was glad for the laughter which came at the moment when he was supposed to give *his*

187

compliment. He just handed the cup to Chitauro. Chitauro was aware that Mhondiwa wasn't saying anything about the beer but he didn't want to press him into saying anything. He was, however, disappointed, and so he looked outside and said: 'It still rains. Lots of crops.'

'It rains to soften the earth for the grave-diggers,' Old Makiwa said.

'As I came down the path,' Mhondiwa said in very soft voice, 'a squirrel crossed my way twice.' It was the first thing he had said on his own since coming into the hut and Chitauro smelt disaster. The atmosphere was becoming too cloggy with the unknown. He said quickly: 'It must have been hunting.'

'Twice,' Mhondiwa repeated emphatically as if accusing Chitauro of lying about a well-known fact. Chitauro winced. The old man groaned. A strange silence fell into the room. Above the silence they heard the roar of the river as it fell over a precipice up in the mountain. It reminded Mhondiwa of lions and suddenly the wind began to blow in the rain through the door. Chitauro sprang up quickly to shut the door. Panic rose in Mhondiwa's chest. He watched the door bang to and something dark and heavy settled softly on his mind. He desperately hoped the feeling would go with the drink.

'I said this beats a woman,' the old man said, downing another cup and cutting Mhondiwa a fresh one. Mhondiwa downed it in one pull and licked his lips with his tongue. Seeing this, an impulse impelled Chitauro to ask: 'Is your wife back yet?' And then he regretted having said it at all, but then he had been certain that Mhondiwa had forgiven him, that Mhondiwa had realized his mistake in thinking that it was he, Chitauro, who had made his wife go away. Chitauro, now realizing his blunder in mentioning Mhondiwa's wife, having mistaken the way in which Mhondiwa had licked his lips after downing that cup as acknowledgement of Chitauro's offer of friendship – and demonstration of forgiveness granted – realizing his mistake, Chitauro felt dark despair settling within him. He too was very afraid of Mhondiwa. He knew where Mhondiwa came from and, in that land, they had the best witchcraft practitioners of any land he had ever heard. Chitauro knew then that he had ruined his chances of ever coming to understand Mhondiwa and win his friendship, and, maybe, his protection.

Chitauro looked up and saw that the old man's eyes were closed as if from some intense internal pain and Mhondiwa's eyes were murky, hiding inscrutable thoughts as he said: 'Did she tell you that she would come back?'

Chitauro knew he had ruined his party and he didn't realize that his attempts to mend it were making it worse: 'No. I just heard that she had gone to see her mother.'

'You should know. She didn't tell me anything. I never talked to her again after the fight. Maybe she talked to you. And if she is coming back I wouldn't presume that she is coming back to me. She made that clear and I understood it as clearly as she said it.' Mhondiwa was getting drunk and the words were not his, or they were his from a long time and distance away. . .

*　　*　　*

She was washing those spare khaki overalls – which were no longer his – whacking them against the rock at the compound washing place, talking with – and down to – the labourers' wives in that condescending and superior manner that became a boss-boy's wife, a way that he had always found embarrassing. He had felt his shame more painfully then, not knowing how to break it to her, knowing how she prided herself in being the boss-boy's wife, and hating her for this pride of hers. So he came towards her, in blue overalls, knowing that she had become silent and that the other women, who hated her superior attitude, were nudging each other in surprised pleasure. But he came on without looking at them and not caring what she might feel.

'Good evening,' he said. She gave the khaki overalls a final savage whack on the washing slab of rock and dropped them. She looked up at him, arms akimbo.

'And so?' she said.

'And so what? I said good evening, didn't you hear me?' She must

189

have already begun to suspect what had happened because her nose was flaring.

'What happened?' she asked.

'Where?'

'You know where.' She liked to pick a quarrel with him when the other women were looking on. So he didn't give her that satisfaction. He washed his hands at the communal washing pond, lapped some water into his mouth, rinsed it and spat the water out, then said: 'Come into the house.'

'I am not till you tell me what has happened.' He looked at her eyes sparking fire, looked at the other women who were now silent, pretending to be busy at their washing when he knew that they were silently praying that he should say what he had to tell her right there at the pond for their wagging tongues to repeat to the other unfortunate women who had remained at home. He knew she too wanted to show the other women how to handle 'a sleepy husband'. Coldly he decided that he wasn't going to give them that satisfaction. He wouldn't admit to himself that he too was a bit afraid of her. He had heard that her mother was the worst witch in her village and she always got what she wanted. They said she had killed her husband when she discovered that the 'husband-softening' medicine she had given him had made him a drooling-at-the-mouth idiot. The daughter had inherited this hard formidable I-get-what-I-want streak from her. Mhondiwa was afraid of her. But as a man, as the husband, he said: 'As you wish,' washed his hands and went down into the lower end of the compound where he got sickeningly drunk, picked up a quarrel with Chitauro, beat the living stink out of him, went back home where he found his wife waiting for him.

'And so that was why you wouldn't tell me what happened, eh?' she asked soon as he entered. He found that she hadn't left him a meal. He would have gone straight to bed without talking to her had she not kept on and on hammering at how thirty-five Mhondiwas were nothing to Chitauro's little finger. He got angry.

'Is he your man that you keep on talking about him?'

190

'O, my! Are you blind as well? I thought you knew. When you look at those children you call yours, do you tap your little tit telling yourself you did the job? Why don't you look at them and see if you could call anyone of them yours? Go ahead! Rumbi! Rumbidzai! Come here and show your father your nose – and you can tell him for me where you got it from.'

He then proceeded to beat her. He didn't know where he hit her but he hit her till she admitted that she had had enough, that she would never do it again. It was the first time he had ever beaten his wife despite her domination of him throughout their married life. His sudden unthinking violence had frightened him. It made him cry. He felt so guilty that he dared not touch his wife as she lay sobbing beside him.

The following morning she was gone, so were her things, and worst and most frightening of all, the lion skin belt he always wore next to his skin, his guardian and protector. He mourned that belt as much as he had mourned his parents long long ago. And from then on he knew he was as weak as a baby.

His wife did not come back. He took the children to Old Makiwa till he could arrange something. The trouble was he couldn't go back home to Mozambique because it was so long ago now since he had left home and then his parents were no longer there. So he scratched his head, trying to think of where he could take his children.

And then he heard that his wife was going round the villages saying that those children were not his but another man's. Some said they had seen her with Chitauro. It was also known that Chitauro had sent his wife home to his parents just about the same time that Mhondiwa's wife left her husband.

Old Makiwa said it was just spiteful rumour but Mhondiwa could see that there was something, a look, in the old man's eyes that betrayed his mouth. And then some of those friends, the men he had done favours when he was still boss-boy, had said words that showed they were afraid of Chitauro but did not clear his name from Mhondiwa's mind. But then Mhondiwa was without his belt and there was nothing he could do since he was now weak. . .

★   ★   ★

'Sorry about that,' Chitauro said into Mhondiwa's murky eyes that hid inscrutable thoughts. He could see that the fear that normally haunted them was now veiled from him. And he was afraid. He looked at the old man, who, thankfully, he saw was about to say something.

'Women,' Old Makiwa said as if he was thinking of something else. It was clear that he was thinking alone to himself but Chitauro found it easier to listen to him than continue his conversation with Mhondiwa who was now staring vacantly into the fire with an empty beer mug in his hand. That Mhondiwa could be unpredictably violent Chitauro very well knew from personal experience. This was the puzzle: that the rather shy, frightened and withdrawn Mhondiwa could be the same man as the unseeingly violent Mhondiwa.

'Women,' the old man repeated. He was too drunk and angry in a private way: hence the monologue. 'There is our death, women. We live because of them and die because of them. It is the woman who wields the whip no matter how we men may fool ourselves into believing we are the masters of our houses.' He drank the beer in his mug, dipped it into the pot and brought it out dripping. 'If I had my life over again I would never marry.'

'It's not possible, Grandfather,' Chitauro said, grateful to talk of women in general and careful not to look Mhondiwa in the eye. 'A man is not a man without a woman.'

Now the old man banged his mug on the floor, spilling some beer: 'It's not a woman that makes a man. It is his luck, his personal protector. A woman is what destroys a man.'

'You forget that you have two wives,' Chitauro said, laughing, concentrating on the old man.

'I no longer have any wife. The younger one went back to her people because the elder one thought that she had come to destroy her home. You see the cunning of a woman? She gives names to

192

everything you haven't bothered to give names to. The home is her own, the children her own and of course you are her own. Nothing is anything unless it is her own.'

Chitauro threw some wood onto the fire and the smoke thickened. Mhondiwa felt like throwing up but he couldn't rise to go out. Old Makiwa came like an oracle out of the smoke: 'She takes everything and leaves you as empty as a mealie husk after the harvest, as undefended as a snail without its shell, and finally, when you are completely broken and useless she sends you out to face the lion without a spear or a shield to defend yourself.'

Old Makiwa's voice had been rising with every word till it was a scream out of the thickening smoke and Mhondiwa's fear also rose with the old man's voice and the smoke till he thought he would burst and the smell that the smoke invoked in the closed room was like something that he desperately wanted to forget but now was forced upon him. . .

★   ★   ★

The sun rose high in the sky that clear cold June morning long ago. The village was almost empty, everybody had gone out for the day and those still at home huddled close to the fire out of the cold. And still his parents had not woken up. There was smoke from the top of the roof of their hut but then that could be from the fire that kept them warm at night.

Mhondiwa went out to milk his one cow – it didn't give much milk because of the cold season. When he came back the door to his parents' room was still closed. He knocked on the door: no answer. He tried to open it but it was bolted tight from inside and all of a sudden he was very afraid. Something told him that something was wrong with his parents. He ran to the nearest neighbours who quickly came with him. They forced the door after several knocks.

In the thick smoke of the room – from a log that had almost burnt itself completely out in the fireplace – they pulled out the bodies of his parents and that of his younger and only brother – who was still a baby.

He couldn't stand the smell in the room – whether it was the smell or the sight of his dead people he couldn't say, but it was a smell that would haunt him all his life – it was something that attacked his bowels and he went out reeling.

The villagers now gathered round the hut, looking at the bodies which were now covered in blankets. There was a sky-shattering wailing.

All that day he stayed away from the house of mourning. But in the evening his father's cousins sent him to his mother's home to inform her people. It wasn't far for grown-ups but for a herd-boy alone at night it wasn't a joke. He had to make the journey through thick jungle with a spear in his hand.

He had gone only a little way into the jungle when he had the feeling that something was following him. He looked back and saw it: a tiny black thing too big to be a cat and too small to be a dog. It seemed to be following him and he began to run. Each time he looked back he saw it and it seemed to be gaining on him. He ran on now oblivious to the fact that he was running, running beyond his age and strength, running beyond thought, on the precipice of a terrible belly-melting fear. He did not look back now but he could feel the thing right on his heels, sniffing at him and he ran on for he couldn't tell how long and he clearly remembered when he fell and that was the end of him. He also remembered calling out some names before he fell.

For two weeks he lay in his grandparents' home, in a restless delirium, haunted by advancing and retreating shadows. He twitched and moaned and raved in his nightmare and no one could reach him and whenever he felt himself breaking out of the jungle into the open something dark pulled him back with the roar of lions – which was the prolonged earth-shaking thundering of a big river falls. And he was drowning and drowning in it. He was all alone for a very long time.

He didn't know it then but Muganu, the medicine-man consulted by his grandparents, worked without cease: pounding and grinding and mixing roots, leaves and bulbs of strange plants, cooking them on the fire that was never put out for two weeks, mixing them with oils and given to the patient through the mouth, the anus, or rubbed into incisions made in his skin; fanning the room with a cowtail dipped in medicine water, chanting the strange words that were the language of the spirit that possessed him, disappearing and reappearing through the dark doorway at night with fresh roots and leaves and plants. Later, when he was beginning to get well, Mhondiwa would feel rather than see all these movements and things vaguely as darker forms in a general darkness, all from a painfully long distance and nothing and no one able to get close to him. Now there was no sharp pain but an all-pervading heaviness in the chest, an awareness at the same time of his being too far away for anyone to reach him and his frantic desire to get up and run and run and run, the despairing heaviness of his limbs and the futility of everything and he would sink again with fearful cries torn out, right out of his guts. And through all this came the smell in his parents' room.

Then slowly, he was becoming better. He would swim lightly into the light and with a will hold the light around him till he felt himself falling into pieces and then he would sink again and always the sinking brought the screams out of him. But he was getting better and one day he was able to speak and the first thing he said was for them to get him out of the dark into the light and so they built a lean-to shelter outside in the open and here he quickly convalesced.

He could now talk and walk but Muganu wasn't yet through with him. There were some other things to be done, things which couldn't have been done while he was delirious.

On that night everybody gathered in Mhondiwa's grandmother's hut to watch Muganu drive out the evil spirit that had caused this sickness in Mhondiwa. They sat up all night till the east was grey. Muganu sweated and the people helped him by chanting. He made several incisions into Mhondiwa's skin and with a suction cup withdrew the bad blood from Mhondiwa's body. There was a pot of herbs brewing on the fire. He took it off the fire and made Mhondiwa kneel near it, his head bent over into it, so that all the fuming steam scaled Mhondiwa's face, then he covered the patient with a blanket so that the fumes from the pot would not escape. Mhondiwa sweated and the steam turned into water on his face but they held him down over the pot. Then Muganu took off the blanket, removed the pot and made Mhondiwa sit on a mat with legs spread out before him. The evil-spirit hunt was on.

Muganu sniffed Mhondiwa all over, as a dog would, and whenever he smelled something he would suck the spot with his mouth to remove the evil talisman, then with the thing in his hand, Muganu would immitate the voice of the one who was purported to have cast the spell and announce the purpose of the bewitching. Then someone would wave a cowtail into Muganu's face and lead him into the night where he would release the talisman and ask it to go back where it came from. The last spell was the hardest to remove. It was a hyena. Muganu laughed like a hyena and almost strangled Mhondiwa to death. The cowtail handler waved it frantically into Mhondiwa's face and the chanting grew wilder and, weakened by the incantations, the 'hyena' was led out into the night where Muganu took a long time in getting rid of it.

Muganu came back into the hut, very exhausted. He had been a long time out and they had heard him howling, going into the jungle, and now he was back, his normal self. He then began the job of strengthening Mhondiwa.

After taking out some powders and roots from his bag, Muganu said to Mhondiwa: 'Very early tomorrow morning before the sun rises go to the river. Strip yourself naked by the water. Stand in the river, facing the rising sun. As the sun rises bathe yourself slowly, rubbing your body with these roots. Address the rising sun; pray to it to give you new life. Get out of the water after throwing these roots on the water so that the river takes them away. Go back to the river again in the evening, before the sun goes down and bathe yourself once more this time facing the setting sun. Ask the setting sun to take away with it all the evil spirits that want to destroy you. After this throw this powder onto the water and let the river carry them to the sea. Then once more face the rising sun, step out of the water and rub your body with this powder. Don't look back into the water. Put on your clothes and come back home. Don't look back.

'When you are back your grandmother will give you some porridge cooked in medicine water. After you have eaten she will give you this belt.

'Now listen carefully about this belt. This belt is lion skin. It should not be seen by anyone except yourself. Don't talk about it to anyone. When you take a wife, she should only feel it about your waist. Don't tell her what it is for. This belt is your guide, your spear and shield in all matters and everywhere you go. It is your personal protector. Respect it and care for it well. Choose a private place on the river – any river wherever you happen to go throughout your life – and here you will have your bath out of sight of anyone. Wear it round your waist, next to your skin. This belt is your best and only friend.'

And slowly Mhondiwa learned to forget his pain and his fear and he believed in the belt. It looked after him on that terrible six-day journey through the wild animal jungle from Gorongozi. Six days and nights of hard jungle travelling, in single file, without rest, eating wild fruits, tree-roots and bark with the hunger-hardened men from his country who were going to seek their fortune in Zimbabwe. He travelled with them in silence and they parted just after crossing the border into Zimbabwe. Some went north towards Inyanga, some south to Melsetter and Chipinge. He and a few others settled near the border round Mutare and Penhalonga. Some found work in the Penhalonga mines and he was employed as a labourer in a forest reserve.

After three years of hard back-breaking work he became boss-boy. He was in charge of a gang of thirty men. He was not married then but he didn't worry because he had the belt.

Then things began to happen to him. He began to feel restless. He often cried alone and at night he couldn't sleep. He began to have visions of his parents in his dreams. He began to think of moving on

197

west, to Harare.

And just at this time he met her, his future wife.

There was a wedding in one of the villages near the forest station. The drums rolled and thudded all night and in that drunken madness of dancing and singing and laughing girls making come-on eyes at the young men of the village he had felt the first stirrings of desire and the emptiness of his life alone. He felt more restless than ever and it was as if there was a little animal trapped inside him that wanted to be released. There was a moon in the sky and he cried, real big man's sobs and he felt ashamed of himself and he fingered the belt restlessly.

Then as he was moving around among the milling people she spoke to him.

'Are you the boss-boy?'

When he said yes he was and she laughed, he knew she was laughing at his accent. They always laughed at him here but he had got used to it. She was with some other girls but he didn't pay any attention to them. She seemed to be in command and so he didn't refuse when she asked him to go with her.

She took him to a musasa shed where she gave him some sadza and beer to drink. He didn't drink then but that night a reckless spirit came into him and he had his first taste of beer. There were many girls all round and they looked at him while he ate and drank. It was as if he were some strange animal on show, but he didn't mind them because he thought they were probably laughing at his accent. They were always laughing at him here but he had got used to it. So he drank and ate and ate and drank and he began to sing songs of his homeland, songs he had long forgotten and didn't know were still in him and the girls laughed till tears stood in their eyes but he didn't mind because he liked the look in her eyes and she was asking him to tell them some of the simple words in his language and they laughed and that pleased him and so it happened that he didn't know when she took him to her mother's place. And when he woke up in the night wondering where he was she held him tight and said it was all right he was at home, at home, at home, she kept on repeating this and it sounded better than

198

anything he had ever heard till then. He thought it was the best sound in the girl's language. And when he cried later towards dawn and she said the words again to him, at home, at home, at home he went with them, following them with something in himself, something that pleased him and he went to sleep for the first time in a long while and it was the first dreamless, most restful sleep of his life.

And so he was already defenceless when, three weeks later, she came up to the forest compound and said that she was carrying his baby. He felt a kind of melting in his belly. His baby. The way she said it made him feel the most mattering man in all her life. And when the baby was delivered five months later and she told him that these things happened with most women – babies were being born face backwards, right side on the left all over the place, he accepted it, after all she was the woman and women knew all sorts of things that went on inside them. And when the village people laughed he knew they were pleased with him because he was a man. . .

*   *   *

Of course he should have heard the bushes and the stones laughing! They knew what was happening and they didn't tell him. Only now, sitting in this room, getting drunk and his chest tightening with the roar of the river, only now did he see it. The baby had been fathered by Chitauro!

'Yes,' Old Makiwa said from a long distance away, 'you only realize too late that she has been sucking you since the day you saw her, lying, lying, lying, destroying and draining the blood out of you, draining the seed out of you, leaving you your empty name whose substances she has used, the empty husk she throws on the ash heap to rot.'

And from a very long distance the river boomed.

Chitauro stood up and went to the door. He opened it and looked out.

'It still rains,' he said.

Old Makiwa's eyes closed. Mhondiwa stared into the fire with his murky eyes that hid inscrutable thoughts. Chitauro hastily made the subject general and innocent of any connotations, general and impossible to misunderstand: 'Listen to the river. It is in flood. The water must be grazing far out from the banks.'

'Tears, tears, and more tears for thirsty, grabbing cruel mother Earth, the hag!' Old Makiwa said, his eyes still closed and sleepily spitting into the fire.

'Life,' said Chitauro pacifically, 'plenty of life.'

'Rain to ease the gravediggers' task,' Old Makiwa said in a very low voice. Chitauro looked back and said quickly: 'You aren't going to sleep, are you?'

'Rain to ease the gravediggers' task,' the old man repeated in the same voice.

Mhondiwa was staring into the fire with his murky eyes that hid . . .

Chitauro summoned up his courage and used his most innocent-of-all-misunderstandings voice, clear as the day is bright: 'Tell me, Mhondiwa, my friend, where does all this rain come from? When we were children we used to call it the tears of God or the other vulgar water our bodies give out, ha ha ha ha!'

In the distance the river crashed and boomed and Chitauro quickly closed the door. When he turned to the fire he saw that Mhondiwa's head was in the process of being adjusted to looking into the fire and he knew with a frightening certainty that those murky eyes had been on him all that time he was standing in the doorway.

Old Makiwa gave a loud snore, chewed nothing in his mouth and began again where the snoring started from, rising in an agonizing crescendo to the moment it would be impossible to go on then he would again chew nothing in his mouth . . .

Chitauro spoke quickly, as if he were giving some last important message to someone who was going away on a bus and the bus was already moving: 'This beer is in your honour. Yes in your honour, my friend, Mhondiwa. I brewed it with my own hands. Couldn't trust anyone to do it knowing how you love *good* beer. You felt how good it was? My mother used to say I have the best hands for beer and if she were here today she would say it again. Now . . . I wouldn't like you to feel that I wronged you. You left your own land and people to come and work here – you don't have to feel you have no friends. I am your friend, Mhondiwa. Yes, the very day I saw you I knew I had a friend. There are differences in languages but never in the heart that understands. I saw you understood people – when you were boss-boy here I never heard anyone say anything but the best about you.'

Now Mhondiwa touched his forehead and Chitauro waxed mellow. He laid his hand on Mhondiwa's knees and said: 'Yes. No matter what people may say I will still –' Quietly Mhondiwa removed Chitauro's hand and brought his head up.

There was nothing in those eyes. Just plain nothing.

Chitauro shrank into himself, some very safe distance from Mhondiwa, into himself.

In the distance the river roared. 'We are friends, Mhondiwa. Our fate is now bound toge –'

Somewhere in the back of his eyes, Mhondiwa saw the tiny black animal cross his path, twice, crash into the jungle, then come back from behind and now it was sniffing his heels. He felt the smoke thickening, rising and curling into tight coils inside his throat and chest and way back beyond memory he felt the river crashing, breaking over the banks and scattering into the jungle.

It was like the roar of lions, the roar of lions, the roar of lions, the roar . . .

'No, no, no, no, no, no, Mhondiwa! We are friends! I didn't touch her! Honestly I didn't! Can't you hear a friend? Can't you . . . No! no, no, no, no, O NO!!!'

In the distance, the river boomed like the roar of lions.

Old Makiwa's snoring reached the peak of its cycle, he stirred, scratched his crotch and went back to sleep, leaving the words 'Did I hearshomethi . . .' trailing behind his mind to catch up with it at some unknown destination.

Mhondiwa stood up slowly, opened the door and went out.

The rain had stopped and the night was warmly-cool with a pleasant breeze from the river. He felt the sticky-warm knife in his hand and decided to wash it in a puddle.

Wisps of clouds. A rainbow-haloed misty moon, the best sound he had ever heard: rest now you are at home, at home, at home . . .

In the distance the river purred.

Mhondiwa walked up the little rise to his house in the forest compound.

He felt at peace with the world.